Eamonn ANDREWS

To Sheila

Eamonn ANDREWS

Tom Brennand

Weidenfeld and Nicolson
London

Contents

Illustration Acknowledgements

The photographs in this book were kindly supplied by the following: The Keystone Collection 2; Popperfoto 7; Gerald Scarfe/*Daily Mirror* 5 above; Syndication International 5 below; Topham Picture Library 3, 8.

The secret fear
of the boy
least likely...

When, in 1964, after fourteen years as one of its most favoured sons, Eamonn Andrews announced he was forsaking the security of the BBC to take his chances with new programme challenges being offered by brash but still insecure ITV, he was lauded as a 'bold and adventurous broadcaster'.

When he also announced that his first venture was to be something completely new to British television and, what's more, at ITV, he was abandoning the safety net of pre-recorded programmes, he was further acclaimed as a courageous trail-blazer of television.

But three months later opinion had changed drastically.

No longer was he being hailed as bold and adventurous or courageous and trail-blazing.

Now the adjectives were rather less polite; now he was being ridiculed as bungling and blustering and even plain embarrassing.

Suddenly the critics had started to crucify him. Viewers, too, were baying for his blood. His shiny new programme, which was, in fact, the first ever 'chat show' to be broadcast on the British television network, had quickly become tarnished and was scandalising the nation.

And not only was Eamonn being blamed for it, he was being subjected to such vituperation as no other broadcaster has ever had to endure in the history of British television.

There were hysterical headlines, jammed switchboards, questions in Parliament and repeated demands to ITV's governing body for the programme to be banned – and Eamonn with it.

He did not deserve all of the blame, of course, but, in truth, he deserved a very large part of it, a proportion of which was perhaps poetic justice. For the bold statements that had brought him those plaudits from the press and public had not been as brave as they had sounded. They had been, in fact, the bold statements of a man putting on a bold face.

Because he had not taken on those challenges by choice but had joined ITV out of sheer necessity. The bald fact was that he had been out of a job. The BBC had killed off both his long-running shows, 'What's My Line?' and 'This Is Your Life', in quick succession and had offered him nothing in place of either.

And where had he landed now Auntie Beeb had kicked him from under her skirts? In 'the rubbish bin of broadcasting' according to one critic's description of his new 'trail-blazing' programme.

The same writer was not alone in describing the programme – called 'The Eamonn Andrews Show' and transmitted late on Sunday nights – as 'a cure for insomnia'.

However, had it been so soporific that some of those 'disgusted' viewers had fallen asleep watching it and, Rip Van Winkle-like, had woken twenty years later – on Guy Fawkes Day, 1987, to be precise – they might well have thought somebody who was a genius, or a saint, or both, had died that morning. The same Eamonn Andrews.

They would have rubbed their eyes at news bulletins and interviews and a special, hour-long, peak-time programme, all as crammed with epitaphs about his expertise as, later, his memorial service at Westminster Cathedral was to be crammed with mourners.

Of his skills, those tributes trumpeted, 'He was the greatest broadcaster of our time' ... 'A giant of radio and television' ... 'A pillar of broadcasting'. And of Eamonn the individual, 'A man of compassion' ... 'A great humanitarian' ... 'A warm and decent human being'.

And, as those awakening viewers watched the parade of television's famous making their gawdy show of trying to analyse how Eamonn attained those professional peaks, they would have heard them pose such questions as: Was it his intelligence? His quick wit? His *supreme* professionalism?

The truth was, of course, that neither a genius nor a saint had died that day.

But clearly a legend had.

Eamonn Andrews *was* one of the first 'Stars' that television made and one of its most enduring.

Whatever his shortcomings he *did* find within himself the resources that took him to the very top of his profession; and he *did* become very wealthy and very famous.

Among the many thousands of words spoken and written on the day of his death, in the succeeding weeks, and at that memorial service in a packed Westminster Cathedral, one point was well made. That was that his achievement was all the more remarkable because few men have ever seemed less likely to achieve such status in the world of broadcasting, of communications, of nation speaking unto nation, than Eamonn Andrews.

For he was born to blush, to be embarrassed, to be pathologically shy, and he grew up almost too timid to speak unto anyone.

But what those paying those tributes did not know was that his achievement was very much more remarkable than that.

It was a secret he kept from most people all his life. He was not just painfully shy of *meeting* people. Throughout the start of his career, and to a decreasing degree in the latter part of it, he actually had a *fear* of people.

He suffered from a condition recognised and given a name by the medical profession only a few years before he died. It is called social phobia and it usually starts to affect its victims when they are in their late teens – as in Eamonn's case – or early twenties.

Social phobia is fear of human contact. The essential nature of it is that those who suffer from it are seized by a seemingly illogical terror of disgracing themselves in the presence of strangers or people they know only casually and in whose company they are afraid they will not feel completely at ease. They do not have attacks when they are alone.

The aspects of his phobia that Eamonn occasionally revealed publicly – because he was powerless to do otherwise – were that social phobics are extra-sensitive to the normal tendencies to blush, or feel overcome by the company or surroundings and have a terror of social occasions from which they cannot make an exit without it being noticed.

Such a situation, or just the mere prospect of it, can cause perspiring, a pounding of the heart, stomach cramps, and even vomiting.

Some sufferers abuse alcohol. To be fair to Eamonn, he could not often be accused of abusing it. But, perhaps understandably, considering the kind of life he lived, he frequently over-indulged in it, particularly in his later years.

Social phobia is, in fact, probably much more common than is realised because people are ashamed to admit to being incapable of controlling the feeling it generates. Nevertheless, it is estimated that one man, and maybe as many as two, in every hundred suffers from it, and that among women there is a slightly higher percentage.

By deliberately seeking to live his professional life in the spotlight, Eamonn may have been courageously submitting himself to the theory held by some psychologists that the only way for the fearful to cope with their fear is to do the very thing that frightens them.

However, although social phobics only feel really comfortable with members of their own family or familiar friends, they are far from loners.

Many are extroverts who seek situations where they can be just that without coming into close contact with strangers in conditions over which they have no control. Eamonn discovered that the radio studio, where his broadcasting career began, was an ideal place in which to be extrovert without being in direct contact with people with whom he was not well acquainted. Television less so – although in many aspects, particularly where the question of control was concerned, it was also the case.

The cause of social phobia is not clear, although there are theories that it often affects people who, in their younger days, have been the subject of severe criticism and also had drilled into them rigid ideas about the way they should behave.

Eamonn certainly experienced those tyrannies, especially in the traumatic early part of his education in Dublin when, a poor scholar and somewhat gawky pupil, he was frequently severely beaten and subjected to a considerable amount of ridicule by his teachers.

His father, too, was partly responsible. Very conscious of his own lack of education and achievement, he tried to live his life vicariously through that of his first born son. Eamonn's only brother, Noel, who was also to become a Radio Eireann sports broadcaster, was ten years younger than him and there were three sisters, two born in the years between himself and Noel and one afterwards.

Despite the meagre wage he earned, his father managed to find enough money to pay for part of Eamonn's schooling at both primary and secondary schools.

Even more important for his ambitions for his son – and, an unheard of state of affairs in the kind of area where they lived – he also paid for Eamonn to have elocution lessons to rid his voice of the harsh, working class Dublin accent with which he and his school pals spoke.

But he was bitterly disappointed by Eamonn's lack of scholastic ability and frequently accused him of being lazy, often threatening him with a thick leather belt which he kept for purposes of chastisement but seldom used (the Christian Brothers more than making up any leeway).

His father also encouraged him to take an interest in classical theatre for which Dublin was then acclaimed and was again disappointed when Eamonn was a failure at acting school and instead, found work on a variety stage as questionmaster of a catch-penny quiz show.

He was disappointed, too, that his son gave up his 'respectable-job-with-prospects' with a leading Irish insurance company to work on sponsored programmes on the new-fangled 'wireless' which was a poor alternative to the theatre or even a good book.

Eamonn's father died in 1950 when Eamonn was twenty-seven years old and just a few weeks after he had made his first broadcast for the BBC, but a year before he appeared on television for the first time.

He had been ill for a long time. But in his autobiography, published in 1963, Eamonn made only the briefest reference to his illness and to his death. He flew to Dublin on the morning of his funeral and caught a plane back to London again that afternoon.

There were a number of other reasons besides his social phobia why Eamonn was a very unlikely person to choose a career in broadcasting.

For one thing he was certainly aware by then that he had little talent as an entertainer – as a singer, dancer or actor – and knew that if he was to succeed he would more than likely have to become very much involved with factual programmes.

5

Yet – and this was another major stumbling block of which he must also have been aware – for some reason he was only capable of taking the flimsiest interest in current affairs, which, of course, provide the raw material for such programmes. He could not be described as a newspaper or magazine reader. He could never be bothered to make the effort to keep up with the news or with trends, and he was never known to study any topical subject in depth.

He rarely felt the need to explain this deficiency but when he did, he blamed it on the fact that he had a poor memory – that was certainly true – and said he saw no point in cluttering or confusing his brain with information he would soon forget anyway, probably before he needed to make use of it.

The production team of 'This Is Your Life' was frequently made aware of how poor his memory was at the weekly production meetings he attended. At one pre-series meeting, after the programme had been revived by Thames Television, it was suggested that as opera singer Dame Eva Turner was about to receive the Freedom of her native town of Oldham, Lancashire, it would be a good idea for Eamonn to surprise her immediately after the ceremony and make a 'This Is Your Life' programme on her as a good *live* opener to the new season.

Eamonn received the suggestion with a frown. 'But an opera singer ... they spend so much time in the theatre and abroad. Do you think she will know the programme?', he asked.

Said the producer, 'She's got to.'

Said Eamonn, 'How are you so sure?'

Said the producer, 'Because you've already done her "Life" once before. This would be a second time. You first had her as a subject in your BBC days.'

When he felt he would really need to know about particular events for any of his programmes, Eamonn relied completely on the members of his production teams to apprise him of them.

This, naturally, left him very vulnerable when, for some reason and it was not an infrequent occurrence, the course of the programme moved beyond the boundaries of his brief.

Poor memory or not, it always remained a mystery why Eamonn did not take more steps at least to try to protect himself from such situations.

One deficiency it was too late to correct and which made him totally unsuited to the chat show, in fact made it the personal disaster that so nearly brought his career crashing down, was the fact that he never learned the art of conversation. He never knew how to fill the silences.

This was very evident off-screen, too, as, during a conversation between groups of even his closest friends, he could be seen shuffling from foot to foot, smiling a lot – and keeping out of it as much as possible.

Companions on anything but the shortest of journeys found it hard work keeping a conversation going as he contributed so little and frequently 'dried up' completely. This also happened during phone calls, even those he initiated, leaving the person at the other end wondering, during the painfully long pauses, if he was still on the line.

But with so much against him, what did Eamonn have going for him?

Well, for one important thing, despite his father's aspirations and those elocution lessons, he still kept in him a lot of the cunning of the Dublin working class kid.

It was not simply that he knew how to ride his luck, he also very soon realised that, to get where he wanted to be from where he was starting out, he would *have* to ride his luck. In the early days he was, to use his own word, a 'chancer'.

A part of his native guile was also his ability to inspire loyalty, often a sympathetic loyalty, from his staff (and viewers). By comparison with most 'stars' he was generally pleasant to work with because – except when he had been drinking – he had a placid disposition and only seldom threw tantrums.

With Eamonn, however, it was not merely a question of what did he have going for him. It was also *who* did he have going for him.

Gary Cooper and Spencer Tracy, that's who. They were the most popular film stars of the 'penny-rush' at the Dublin picturehouses of his youth, the 'gentle giants' of his favourite films of the Forties, 'Sergeant York' and 'Boys' Town', and later he deliberately tried to imitate their screen images.

The fact that he had won the Irish Junior Amateur Middleweight Boxing Championship in his late teens was a great help.

It gave him a reputation for toughness. So he, too, like his boyhood heroes, Cooper and Tracy, could pretend to be the tough guy with the gentle and folksy nature.

Whenever the word 'Junior' was accidently dropped from a reference to the boxing title he did not bother to correct it. When 'Amateur' was forgotten, too, he did not rush to disillusion anybody who was prepared to believe he had been sufficiently skilled to have won it in the professional ranks.

But what Eamonn had going for him most was that he was a realist. He was able to face up to the fact that it was his brogue and not his brain that got him his first all-important job in British broadcasting. That and those two-bob-a-term elocution lessons.

For when he applied for a job at the new, democratised, postwar BBC in 1950, after a little experience with the fledgling Radio Eireann, they realised his was the classless accent which, by then, they now wanted.

Even to Irish ears it was not definable by class. Sensibly he had not tried to Anglicise it. Nor his name, either. Plain Edward or Eddie Andrews – which is what it would have been in English – would not have been the same thing at all. (In private, his wife called him 'Himey', although she denied it was an ironic nickname born out of any anti-semitic sentiments he might have had).

At the time of his audition, BBC thinking had also already been conditioned by the success of the similarly 'neutral', mid-Atlantic voice of broadcaster Stewart MacPherson, who was returning to his native Canada and whom Eamonn succeeded as questionmaster of a cod quiz programme, 'Ignorance Is Bliss', and later as their boxing commentator.

Commenting shortly afterwards on Eamonn's 'voice neutrality', a journalist wrote, 'He comes across to the listener as classless and therefore not one of THEM.'

He went on: 'Natural, neutral, inoffensive, unaffected, uncommitted . . . if you tried to assemble the perfect middleman by Identikit you would come up with someone remarkably like Eamonn Andrews.'

And he added: 'Nobody could accuse him of having a dangerous quantity of sex appeal, either.'

The fact that he betrayed no special knowledge of current events was also the subject of newspaper comment. But it did not prove to be a handicap in Eamonn's attempt to establish himself in broadcasting. 'Ignorance Is Bliss', required him to do little more than deliver scripted feed-lines for the three comic panellists' scripted gags.

Nor did he need to read much more than the sports pages to prepare himself for his boxing commentaries. In any event, thanks to the interest he had taken in it as a youngster, boxing was the one subject on which he could be said to be really knowledgeable.

It also gave him a set of references he otherwise lacked and was, in fact the only subject on which I heard him speak with complete confidence in the whole twenty-two years of our association.

Yet, there was no denying the huge success he had, a success that surprised even himself. When he was at the peak of it he was candid enough to write, 'It is a constant source of amazement to me that what I do is something which can earn me a living.'

He was not always able to be so honest, however. He was conscious that his career was something of a television accident which could only have started when it did, and how it did, and was ever fearful that one day he would be 'found out'. There were times when, to stay at the peak he reached comparatively early in his career, sadly he found he had to lie, even to cheat; although, over the years, he appeared to become disposed to such a degree of self-deception that he was able to persuade himself either that he was not committing any such transgressions or he was entirely justified in doing so if he was.

Someone who made a very accurate assessment of the reason for Eamonn's popularity was Bill Cotton, when he was managing director of the BBC. In a programme about TV success, transmitted just before Eamonn died, Cotton said of him, 'He sells an ordinariness. The British public quite like that. They like to think they could do what you can do if they like you.'

There were many millions of such viewers like that who were fans of Eamonn, although many of them would never admit it to their neighbours. For Eamonn would have been the first to agree that he was a hero of the hapless, the patron saint of stumblers.

The fact that he *did* inspire some viewers in the way Cotton suggested was once demonstrated to him personally, not by someone who was a fan himself but was the son of someone who clearly recognised his achievements.

He was a room-service waiter, a young and, Eamonn suspected, slightly tipsy Irishman, at a hotel in Manchester, who suddenly realised the guest he was serving was his famous countryman. But he was far from overawed. 'You know, it's all your fault I'm here,' he said, accusingly.

When Eamonn politely inquired why, the waiter explained that while he was out of work in Ireland he had got into an argument with his mother.

'She started shouting at me to go over to England and make my fortune,' he went on.

'I told her I didn't know that I could do that and she said, "Why not? Eamonn Andrews did!" So that's why I'm here doing this!'

And with that he slapped down the tray of drinks and weaved his way out without even waiting for a tip.

It was when Eamonn had moved on to programmes where an awareness of current events was considered to be a distinct advantage, if not a complete necessity, that his colleagues started to become familiar with his extraordinary childlike naivety and puzzling determination to remain cocooned from the world around him.

Some, who shared his father's views without realising it, thought it was due to an inherent laziness which caused him to prefer to leave it to others to do such work for him.

Executives at ABC Television (later Thames TV) got a shock after they had persuaded him to sign a very lucrative three-year contract for the chat show. So much so that, just a few months after it had gone on air, the head of the department responsible for the programme felt compelled to write a memo to its production team about their new star, who had already been in broadcasting for more than twenty years and in television for thirteen, which read:

'Not only should adequate research be done, but it should be seen to be done by Eamonn.

'We must continue our unrelenting efforts to improve Eamonn's technique on air.

'The senior administration is aware of our friend's problems – we must do our damnedest to improve him.'

However, they were in for a worse shock when they realised Eamonn took only a scant interest in the theatre and practically none in the cinema, or that he had never grown to accept that watching television was part of the price that had to be paid for appearing on it. Or at least watching the kind of programmes that he really needed to know about in the job he was doing.

For they were very sensitive to the fact that, however unappealing show business might be to some – and Eamonn appeared to treat it with total disdain – it was a staple of the success of the chat show. Johnny Carson's 'Tonight' show in America, on which 'The Eamonn Andrews Show' had been modelled, had already proved that to be the case.

Eamonn so much eschewed not only show business but show business people that the only connection his best friend in London for thirty years had with them was that he occasionally buried one. He was an undertaker.

He was, in fact, so disinterested that before a 'This Is Your Life' programme about even the most famous screen celebrity he usually had to be shown a photograph of the 'star' in case in the 'surprise' confrontation he leapt out on the wrong person.

Frequently this lack of interest caught him out. Although actor Charlton Heston had starred in many film epics, it was years later that he made his debut on the London stage. By then he had, if anything, become even more of a household name as the star of the American soap opera 'The Colbys', and this prompted the then producer of 'This Is Your Life' to suggest they should make a programme about him while he was in England.

But Eamonn was totally against it. Somewhat irritated by the suggestion, in fact. 'We don't want to be making "Life" programmes about American actors!' he stormed. 'We should be going after big British stars. People like Sir Ralph Richardson.'

'That could be rather difficult,' said the producer.

'Why should it?' demanded Eamonn.

'Because,' said the producer, 'Sir Ralph Richardson died a year ago.'

What Eamonn did not know, either, was that while he had been alive Sir Ralph had given strict instructions to Lady Richardson not to let him get anywhere near him with his famous big red book.

It was one of the many things that were deliberately kept from him so as not to undermine his confidence, that a number of theatre people, like Sir Ralph, held him in similar disdain as that in which he, himself, held people in the less exalted reaches of the entertainment industry.

He never knew, for instance, that when that great lady of the British theatre, Dame Peggy Ashcroft, was asked to appear on a

'This Is Your Life' about a good friend of hers, actor Harry Andrews, she declined with the reason, 'I cannot be associated with anybody so lacking in talent and class as Eamonn Andrews.'

Nor was he ever aware that it was only after a great deal of persuasion that Sir John Gielgud eventually agreed to appear on a 'This Is Your Life' featuring the doyenne of actresses Cathleen Nesbitt, but made the pre-condition. 'Whatever happens I must not be asked a question by *that person!*'

This was agreed, and on the day of the show Eamonn was told that Sir John was always a 'self-starter' – once introduced he would prefer to go straight into what he intended to say about Miss Nesbitt without being cued by the usual question.

Eamonn accepted the production team's explanation that this was one of Sir John's 'little peculiarities'. But he insisted that he must be told with what words Sir John intended to finish his tribute, so he would know when to go on with the next part of the programme.

When one of the team conveyed this request to Sir John he replied in those famous fluted tones, 'Tell him I am an *act-or*! He will know I have finished when my lips stop moving!'

On the night of the show, as he was being driven to the studio, Sir John suddenly realised he was about to arrive half an hour early. He was horrified. There was plenty of time in which to come face to face with Eamonn before the programme started and feel obliged to talk to him! So he ordered the chauffeur to keep driving around the block until there were only a couple of minutes to go and he knew Eamonn would be safely out of the way, waiting to walk onto the set.

On an earlier occasion a researcher phoned Sir John and asked him if he would be kind enough to take part in a 'This Is Your Life' programme on an actor acquaintance of his, Brian Blessed. To which Sir John replied, 'Why, is he dead?', and put the phone down.

Actor and director Sir John Clements was prepared to go to even greater lengths than Gielgud to avoid a behind-the-scenes meeting with Eamonn when he was eventually coaxed into appearing on the 'Life' of actress Kathy Staff, who was starring as 'Nora Batty' in the television comedy series 'Last Of The Summer Wine'.

First of all he insisted he was not to be brought on until at least halfway through the programme (he was, in fact, intended to be the final big name 'surprise') and that the car sent to convey him to the studio was timed to arrive at least two minutes after it had started. Then he instructed that the car also be ready and waiting at the nearest exit when the programme finished so he could make a fast getaway the moment the cameras were switched off.

As things turned out, Sir John, who lived in Brighton, was taken ill a few days before the programme and was not able to make the journey. So new arrangements had hastily to be made for an alternative stirring 'pay-off'.

Apart from his lack of popularity among the higher echelons of the theatre, there were other reasons why Eamonn seemed so unlikely to succeed in his particular area of television, the least of which was that he suffered more than his fair share of spoonerisms, such as declaring with great conviction on her 'Life' that Sixties glamour girl Diana Dors made her film debut in 'The Slop At Shy Corner'.

Another was that he did not have the ability to ad-lib, to 'think on his feet'.

Whenever he slipped out of the carefully prepared script, or lost his place, members of his back-up team held their breath. For he so frequently talked himself into trouble.

He ventured off his script briefly during an early 'This Is Your Life' programme at the BBC about Coco the Clown and the result became a television legend.

During the programme he brought on a youngster who had lost a leg after being knocked down by a car and whom Coco had visited in hospital.

As scripted – everything guests said on 'This Is Your Life' was carefully written and rehearsed – the youngster thanked Coco for going to see him in hospital. But then Eamonn made an extempore remark. 'Now little man,' he said to the boy, 'you'll think twice before you run across the road next time, won't you?'

He talked himself into more embarrassment on 'What's My Line?' when he was interviewing the film actor Omar Sharif about the fact that he had recently taken up residence in France.

'But what about living in Paris?' he asked him. 'I mean, with a face like yours presumably you can't go out-of-doors?'

Annoyingly for Eamonn, he was repeatedly reminded right throughout his television career of the on-air bloomers he made. In

1986 as part of the celebrations to mark the fiftieth anniversary of television, the BBC showed a 'This Is Your Life' of which Harry (later Sir Harry) Secombe was the subject and which had been made twenty-eight years before.

It was painful enough for Eamonn to be reminded that when, as the climax to the programme, he reassembled the 'Goons' and after getting Spike Milligan's name correct he then, for some reason, went on to introduce Peter Sellers as Eric Sykes.

But what was far more embarrassing was that the re-run programme reminded him – and millions of viewers – that while movingly talking about Secombe's wartime experiences he declared, 'You were in action in North Africa, Sicily, Italy and *Australia*'. Exgunner Secombe needed all the self-control he could command to stop himself bursting into laughter at what was supposed to be a most solemn moment in the programme.

However, Eamonn frequently suffered even greater agonies than mere slips of the tongue when he was talking to famous personalities. His biggest worry – after his fear of failing to be able to recognise them – was getting their names right.

A few weeks after the start of the chat show, I managed to persuade The Beatles, the biggest entertainment attraction in the world at that time, to be guests on the programme. And not only were they to sing and play two of their latest hit songs live, they also agreed, for the first time ever, to be interviewed – and at length – as a group. With the interview and their music contribution they would, in fact, take up the whole of the programme.

It was a considerable coup for the infant programme. But minutes after the show started it became clear Eamonn thought Ringo Starr was George Harrison – and vice versa – and, to the delight and derision of John Lennon and Paul McCartney, he started addressing Ringo as George.

Occasions when names were his nemesis followed in abundance on both 'The Eamonn Andrews Show' and subsequent programmes. But at least it could have been said of him that he forgot or mixed up the names of the famous so frequently he could never be accused of taking pains to puff up their egos.

In just a few notable interviews he addressed Roy Kinnear throughout a programme as Willie Rushton, gave Irish broadcaster Gloria Hunniford the name of American film actress Gayle

Hunnicut, and kept calling Gina Lollabrigida by the name of that other well-proportioned Italian actress Sophia Loren – never once realising his mistake, even though every time he called her Sophia 'La Lollo' jokingly glanced over her shoulder, pretending she thought Miss Loren had just walked in behind her.

Eamonn's tendency for mixing up names and people was so prevalent that when 'This Is Your Life' featured black actress Nina Baden-Semper members of the production team realised there was a terrible inevitability that when he came to say her name he would get it wrong, but were powerless to do anything about it. Consequently, at the end of the programme they were mortified but hardly surprised when he handed her the red book and solemnly declared, 'This Is Your Life . . . Nina Baden-Powell'.

On another occasion, no matter how hard they tried they could not stop him making a blunder of the same, if not greater pro-portions, when he introduced world-renowned baritone Tito Gobbi as a guest on a 'This Is Your Life' of British opera singer Rita Hunter.

When he rehearsed Gobbi's introduction without him being present he kept confusing his name with that of a popular postwar band leader, whom he knew personally, and repeatedly introduced him not as Tito Gobbi but as Tito Burns.

Each time he made the mistake one of the production team corrected him. Then, in his dressing room just before the show, he repeated the right name aloud over and over again to get it firmly fixed in his mind.

And when the show started, and he gave Gobbi his introduction, there were almost audible sighs of relief when he managed to get the name right. But by the time he had to ask him the question that would cue the singer into his 'tribute' to Miss Hunter, he had got his mind into such a tangle again that he inverted his first name and his surname,

And, instead of merely getting his name wrong, he came out with what sounded like a very personal comment about the size of the Italian's mouth.

For his question began, 'Well now, Gobbi . . .'

Other people's names were not the only ones Eamonn frequently forgot though. He often had great difficulty remembering his own name – at least the one he was supposed to be using temporarily for 'This Is Your Life' security purposes.

Whenever members of the team had reason to fear a mention of his real name might betray to an eavesdropper something of what they were planning, they referred to him as 'Fred'.

And whenever the show was being produced at a regional studio he was, for the same reason, booked in to his hotel under a false name.

That made life 'on the road' even more difficult for a person with a memory like his and once when, amidst all the usual cloak-and-dagger secrecy, he went with the programme to Bristol to spring the surprise, he gave away his true identity almost immediately.

He was booked into his hotel as Mr Richard Jackson and, shortly after he arrived there, he called room service for some drinks. Then, as it happened to be the evening the programme was transmitted, he settled down in his suite to watch the one he had recorded a week earlier.

Normally when he was trying to keep his identity secret and he summoned a hotel's room-service he would listen for the waiter's knock, call out in a disguised voice that he was in the bathroom and tell him to let himself in.

Then he would scurry behind the bathroom door, shout more phoney voice instructions to the waiter to leave the order in the sitting room, and put a hand around the door for the bill to sign – a wet hand if he felt in a really big acting mood.

But that evening in Bristol he became so preoccupied with watching the 'Life' of his old friend Katie Boyle he did not hear the knock. Then, startled by a movement behind him, he instinctively looked around and found himself staring straight at the waiter who had let himself in with his pass key.

The waiter, too, was startled as he found himself looking at a Mr Richard Jackson who bore such an uncanny likeness to a Mr Eamonn Andrews. Then he glanced at the television screen. Then again at 'Mr Jackson'. Now convinced, he said, 'You're Eamonn Andrews, aren't you?' Then, before Eamonn could reply, and to his increased discomfort, he asked, 'Do you *always* watch yourself on television?'

Eamonn did not answer that and, instead, grabbed the bill from the waiter's hand. But he was so flustered he could not recall the name under which he had been booked in. He made a stab at it and signed the bill not Richard Jackson but J. Richards, at which the waiter stared in more puzzlement.

Shortly after the waiter had left, the phone rang and Eamonn, who was expecting calls only from his producer, was surprised to hear the caller ask, 'Is that the Richard Jackson I used to know in Dublin?'

Now completely flustered, he snapped impatiently, 'No, my name's Eamonn Andrews' – before realising the caller had obviously been put up to it by the waiter.

And that it was the third name he had used since he had arrived at the hotel less than an hour before.

However, when it came to remembering names, he could make life even more embarrassing for himself than that.

A few years before he left the BBC, the Queen made a visit there to mark the twenty-fifth anniversary of the start of the television service in Britain and, as a young mother, she watched an edition of the children's programme 'Crackerjack'.

As the programme's host, Eamonn presented her with silver propelling pencils – instead of the normal 'Crackerjack' pencils he gave to children who appeared on the show – for young Prince Charles and Princess Anne.

He was then about to present her with an Andy Pandy doll for the infant Prince Andrew. But at that very moment he completely forgot the prince's name.

'Your Majesty, this is for ...' he said, and stopped.

The Queen waited politely, giving him time to recover.

'This is for ...' he said again, and again he stopped and started to perspire.

This time the Queen came to his rescue. 'For the little one, Mr Andrews,' she said.

'Yes, ma'am,' said a relieved Eamonn. 'This is for ... the little one.'

Once again Eamonn cursed himself for that nervous failing; that lack of finesse or self-confidence which could turn relatively straightforward events into occasions of nail biting suspense.

He had plenty with which to console himself, however. At least the working class kid from Dublin *had* met the Queen of England.

And there were to be many more such memorable moments in a career that had barely begun.

There would, of course, also be quite a few he would want to forget.

2

Beatings, boxing, broadcasts, and . . . 'The Moon is Black!'

Eamonn was born six days before Christmas 1922, the son of a carpenter, in a Dublin where barefoot urchins still roamed the streets and black-shawled women – the 'shawlies' – held out their hands to beg for ha'pennies.

He was the first of five children of devoutly religious parents, Willie and Margaret Andrews, and home was a cramped upper floor flat in a plaster-peeling Victorian terrace in Synge Street. The flat stood pick-a-back atop the basement flat below, its front door reached by a steep flight of stone steps up which, each night, his father, in faded blue overalls and wearing steel rimmed spectacles, manhandled the old bicycle on which he rode to and from his job with – ironically, as the flat was lit by gas – the city's Electricity Supply Board.

Willie Andrews was an only son of an only son and a slight, never-very-strong, sensitive man who smoked a lot and drank but little.

Throughout his life Eamonn had a proper respect for his father but never gave the impression he felt any real warmth for him as he did for his mother, who was an altogether less demanding parent.

Willie had set out to improve on his own lack of learning before Eamonn was born. To this end, he battled with his shyness – as Eamonn would have to himself to an even greater degree – to become an amateur actor and play producer. On the billboards and programmes he called himself Will Andrews.

One of Eamonn's earliest recollections as a child, in fact, was being taken to the church hall after Sunday Mass when his father was rehearsing, and the feeling of embarrassment that came over him when he started to declaim his lines. His father's favourite acting roles were in melodramas and religious plays.

Despite that embarrassment, however, his father's interest in the stage gave Eamonn an early ambition to be a playwright. There were two other contributing factors, his belief that George Bernard Shaw had been born in Synge Street and that the street got its name from the famous Irish dramatist John Millington Synge.

It was a fact that Shaw had been born at the other, more affluent, end of the street, but many years later Eamonn discovered the less-than-glamorous truth that the street was named after its not-so-famous local builder. By then, and having made one attempt at it, he had, anyway, long given up hope of becoming Synge Street's second Shaw.

When he was five, and his mother was expecting her second child, the family moved to a council house with three bedrooms, one of which Willie converted into a bathroom, on an estate not far away.

In later years Eamonn was inclined to romanticise about the poverty his family had to endure in the Dublin of the Twenties and Thirties, recalling how 'a scrape of butter' on the bread, instead of dripping, was frequently a luxury. But schoolfriends remembered the family as being as well off as any and, in a part of the city where many children went barefoot, he was dressed better than most.

Again it was Willie's determination that Eamonn would not grow up as just another Dublin street kid.

Somehow he also even managed to enrol him at infants' school as a private pupil, paying 2/6d a term to the Sisters of The Holy Faith for his early education at their convent in the oldest part of the city, a quarter called the Liberties.

The fee granted the private pupils some privileges over the poorer non-fee paying pupils in the national section of the convent school. For one thing it meant the five-year-old Eamonn could use the splendid Georgian front entrance while the non-fee payers had to enter and leave by the 'back door' further along the road.

This sowed seeds of snobbery in the young Eamonn which later in life, and despite the modest, Mister Everyman image he carefully projected in public, he frequently revealed in his private life. He developed an ardent admiration for the aristocracy to an extent that many who knew him in private life considered him to be something of a social climber. And in private, too, he did not even attempt to disguise a disdain for the mass of viewers who had secured his success.

In fact, he once partly betrayed this attitude in public when, in an unguarded moment during a television programme not long before his death, he described some young autograph-hunters he had recently encountered as, 'A bunch of snotty-nosed kids clutching their stubs of pencils and bits of grubby lavatory paper'.

In the first floor schoolrooms which overlooked, but were a safe distance away from, the teeming tenement buildings of Dublin's notorious Coombe district, he was a popular pupil with the nuns. They taught him to read and to count and prepared him for his First Communion at the nearby church of St Teresa, where, at the age of seven, the earliest permitted, Eamonn became an altar boy.

Later he was to admit to the memory that it was the thought of donning the altar boys' scarlet soutane and white surplice, and being seen by the whole congregation on the other side of the altar rails, as much as any feeling of piety that attracted him to the idea.

Life changed dramatically the following year, however, when he moved to a school not far from the family's former home in Synge Street and which was run by an order of the Christian Brothers, which ruthlessly pursued scholastic achievement in its charges.

He was a shy and gawky boy, big for his age, and initially a very poor scholar, coming bottom of the class in his first year there.

As a consequence he was beaten many times, sometimes brutally, with the purpose-made thick, leather strap, with rigid handle, with which the Brothers meted out punishment, secure in the knowledge that even if they disagreed with it Catholic parents would not complain of the activities of members of a religious order.

Eamonn's parents certainly never would. They went to Mass every day and Eamonn and the other children followed suit. Frequently, on his way home from school, Eamonn would also call in at St Teresa's and spend a few minutes at prayer.

Ironically, it was because of his attempts to avoid more beatings from the Christian Brothers that one day he suffered an even more ignominious hiding from a smaller classmate, but one that was to have an important influence on his whole future life.

Seldom able to master the set homework, Eamonn would go into school half an hour early and try to copy it from the exercise books of other pupils.

During one of these cribbing sessions, however, he got into an argument with the smaller boy and they started to fight.

At first Eamonn was confident that, with his superior height and weight, he would soon vanquish his opponent. But within seconds his face was covered in blood and he was relieved when other pupils thought they heard a master approaching and pulled the two apart.

Eamonn had to rush to the toilet in the school yard to wash away the blood and while he was holding his head under the cold water tap he resolved he would never suffer such intimidation again; he would learn the art of boxing.

That same evening he joined a boxing club and for the next 18 months he went there at least three nights a week.

At around the same time Eamonn also became, at the age of ten, a member of the school choir and it was then, in fact, that his voice was heard on the radio for the first time, albeit among thirty other boys, in a music festival which was broadcast by Radio Eireann. Afterwards he harboured a second ambition that he would one day become a famous singer.

That lasted as long as twenty years, until one day his big chance came – and ended in disaster.

By that time his career in broadcasting was proceeding at a remarkable pace. He was already presenting 'This Is Your Life', 'What's My Line?' and the top children's programme, 'Crackerjack', on BBC Television and 'Sports Report' and 'Housewives' Choice' on radio. It seemed he could not fail. But when, in addition, he was given the opportunity of introducing a television variety show he was persuaded by a producer, who knew of his ambition, to use it as a vehicle from which to launch himself as a singer.

The shortest singing career in show business history began and ended on the very first edition of the programme which, like his later chat show, was also called 'The Eamonn Andrews Show'.

His first song, in which he was accompanied by two established female vocalists of the day, one named Jill Day and the other using the single name of Yana, was called 'You May Not Be An Angel'.

It immediately proved he certainly was not a singer, because from the moment the first note left his lips he was singing off key.

Protesting viewers were already blocking the telephone lines when, even more wildly out of tune, he started to sing a solo number, 'How Deep Is The Ocean?', into which his singing career then sank without trace.

The experience did not blunt his ego sufficiently to prevent him making a record, however. A few years later he was persuaded to 'talk' his way through a song on disc. It was called 'Shifting, Whispering Sands' but it was to come screaming back into his brain time after time in years to come and haunt him for the rest of his days as radio disc jockeys played it repeatedly under such collective headings as 'The worst record ever made', 'The world's most dire disc', or even 'A song to puke to'.

Eamonn's scholastic performance at Synge Street School was a great disappointment to his father. Most children left at fourteen to become apprenticed to a trade as Willie himself had. Those parents who wanted their offsprings to stay on for another four years and take the prestigious Leaving Certificate, the equivalent of the British matriculation, had to pay school fees.

By then there were four more children for Willie to provide for. He could just about manage the fees of four pounds a year but to pay for Eamonn's keep together with his school clothing and text books, for four further years out of his earnings of less than £200 a year while keeping the rest of the family clothed and fed, would be impossible.

So Willie gave Eamonn an ultimatum. He would pay for him to attend school for one more year because that was also a scholarship year. If Eamonn passed the scholarship he would stay for three more years to take the Leaving Certificate. If he failed he would leave immediately and become an apprentice to a trade or take a non-skilled job as a shop assistant or delivery man or whatever else he could find.

Almost miraculously, the ultimatum worked. For the best part of a year Eamonn lived a near-monastic life, locked away each evening and almost every weekend in the tiny front room of the council house trying to absorb lessons on English, Irish, Latin, History, Geography, Mathematics and Chemistry. Being no academic he had to work harder than most. English, especially essay writing, was the one subject in which he felt any measure of confidence. But the following summer his parents were notified that he had passed the scholarship.

By then, already on the next part of the Eamonn-moulding process, his father had persuaded him to take an interest in not only his own amateur theatricals but in the professional theatre, taking him on regular visits to Dublin's famous Abbey, Gaiety and Gate theatres.

The next step was to rid the adolescent Eamonn of the harsh Dublin working class accent which, despite Willie's Thespian-type coaching and his secondary school education, was still very evident in the way he spoke.

So, besides school fees, Willie somehow managed to find enough money to pay for elocution lessons. In securing a future for his eldest son it was the best money he ever invested.

Because from that moment Eamonn started to soften those harsh Dublin vowel sounds and cultivate the accent that was to talk him into the BBC.

It was fortunate, too, that, despite the harshness of his surroundings he had no trouble carrying out Willie's wishes because his burgeoning reputation as a boxer dissuaded any of the other boys from ridiculing him as an effete sissy for taking the elocution lessons as they would with any other kid in the neighbourhood.

His English teacher learned of the elocution lessons and approved. To encourage him further he got Eamonn to read out his own essays in front of the class. Eamonn found he enjoyed being the centre of attraction on these occasions as much as he had when he was an altar boy, and still was in a boxing ring.

It encouraged him in his writing, too. He started to enter essay writing competitions in Irish magazines and, to his amazement, one of them won him the first prize of a bicycle. The subject was hair oil.

He decided he would try to write for cash. Using his knowledge as an amateur boxer he wrote a piece called 'How To Train For A Fight' and sent it to the *Evening Herald* in Dublin who published it with his by-line and paid him a guinea.

With these two successes and the glory of seeing his name in print, Eamonn decided nothing could stop him from becoming the greatest literary lion of all time. Now he had dreams of not only emulating, even surpassing, Dublin playwrights Shaw and Synge but also Dublin poet W. B. Yeats.

But he did not want the minds of those who were going to gasp in amazement at his poetic genius to be preconditioned by the journalistic 'pot-boilers' he foresaw he would have to write until he got himself established.

So he decided that for this purpose he must adopt a poetic pen name and, perhaps subconsciously hoping some of their artistic skill would rub off on his poetry, to borrow it from the actor and actress he most admired on his outings to Dublin's theatres, Michael MacLiammóir and Meriel Moore.

Thus was born Michael Meriel, poet of this parish.

Under that nom-de-plume and perhaps riding his winning streak on the subject of hair, or at least of hair oil, he penned a poem about a small boy's first visit to a barber shop which he sent to the magazine 'Hibernia' and which, to his delight, they eventually had the sense to publish.

Then he waited for the payment he expected of at least one guinea. And waited and waited. It never came. He was not at all amused when his pal, fellow poet, and critic Joe Reynolds, who was himself to become a success as a writer, suggested that Hibernia had probably sent half a guinea to Michael MacLiammóir and the other half to Meriel Moore.

And thus died the poet Michael Meriel.

During this heightened literary period Eamonn's interest in boxing never waned. In fact he became such an enthusiast that he would miss an evening at the theatre if a big boxing match was being broadcast, which was becoming a more frequent event then, in the late Thirties. Listening to the commentaries gave him yet another ambition, his fourth after playwright, singer, and poet. He now decided he wanted to become a boxing commentator.

He wrote to Radio Eireann and asked them for an audition. In his letter he declared, 'I am an expert in boxing and I have studied elocution.' He omitted to mention that he was only sixteen and still at school.

It worked. A few months later he got a letter inviting him to auditions that were being held during an amateur tournament at the National Stadium. He prepared himself for them by writing out his own 'commentaries' from reports of prizefights in newspapers and magazines and reading them aloud in his bedroom using a hairbrush as a pretend microphone.

The preparation paid off. At the auditions, which were made in the commentary box on a balcony looking down on the ring, he managed to talk non-stop throughout the three one-and-a-half minute rounds.

He felt he had done well. But the Radio Eireann representatives merely said, 'Thank you. We'll let you know.' It was three years before they did.

At the end of his last year at school he managed, to his parents' relief, to scrape through his Leaving Certificate. It served its intended purpose by securing him a 'respectable' white-collar job, thanks to his English teacher who put in a word for him with friends there, at the Hibernian Insurance Co. in Dublin.

His first job there was as a £60 a year filing clerk, retrieving clients' files from ancient cabinets in the stone basement of the building at the demand of more senior clerks, and later returning them to the same place.

After he had been doing this a few months, Eamonn became so bored with finding the correct destination for returned files he started to dump them in one of a number of brand new cabinets, which had not yet been brought in to use, and spend the rest of the time in the adjacent furnace room reading, and smoking Sweet Afton cigarettes.

His theory was that once files had been needed for reference the chances were that they were unlikely to be wanted again for a considerable time; his intention was that he would file them properly at a later date when he felt more in the mood for it.

Neither his theory nor his intention worked the way he had anticipated.

His new system was so much easier than the official one that soon the first unused cabinet was overflowing with files and he had started to dump them into a second one. Before long the unfiled files were beginning to rival the properly filed files in both numbers and occupied territory.

Inevitably, he began to find that an increased number of the files that senior clerks demanded he bring them urgently were not in their proper places, from which they could quickly be retrieved, but somewhere among the mass of paperwork he had tossed into the new cabinets. It was through all this chaos he had to search for them.

Inevitably, too, his seniors began to notice the frequency with which he was taking much longer than usual to return with the files they had asked for. With his so-often repeated excuse that the documents had been 'slightly misfiled' the shamefaced, perspiring Eamonn was beginning to condemn himself, for by that time it must have been him who had been the misfiler.

Eventually the office supervisor called for an investigation and the file-mountain was discovered. Eamonn found himself standing in front of the general manager's desk.

'Are you lazy or dishonest or what, Andrews?' he asked him.

Realising he had no alternative Eamonn replied quickly, 'Lazy, sir.'

To his relief the general manager told him he would be allowed to keep his job provided he sorted out the filing system in his own spare time. For weeks he stayed at the office after hours until it was finally back in order again.

But it was not all gloom at the Hibernian Insurance Company. Eamonn became friendly with three other young clerks, one of whom was Jack MacGowran, later to become an Irish actor of international repute, and in his first summer there the four rented a holiday chalet on a hillside overlooking Dublin Bay and near the little seaside town of Howth, eight miles north of the city.

From there they cycled back to the office in Dublin every day throughout the summer months and in the evenings they explored the seashore and the countryside.

It was an idyllic time, so idyllic that Eamonn fell in love. Or, at least, thought he did.

Her name was Trixie and in later years he remembered her romantically as being a mysterious, gipsy-like girl, almost impossible to pin down, whom he used to see walking barefoot and alone through the foam.

The truth was that she was a fairly ordinary, quite pretty dark-haired girl who lived in an ordinary house on top of the hill above the chalet and occasionally went to the dances, the 'hops' or 'socials' as they were called, that were held in the local church hall.

Eamonn went to the dances too, but never asked Trixie to dance. In fact he did not ask any girl to dance. Sadly for him, nineteen-year-old Eamonn was feeling the first symptoms of social phobia, the illogical fear of close contact with strangers with which he was to struggle for many years.

A close friend of his at that time later said, 'Eamonn was so shy among strangers that he couldn't speak. He would blush and look away from them and because he thought they knew he was blushing he would blush even more. It was a terrible handicap for him but one he tried to grit his teeth against and kept fighting.'

Sometimes Eamonn would walk up the hill alone and just gaze at the house where Trixie lived and, at the time, he tried to describe his feelings in a poem, 'Pilgrimage':

> Up the seven hills, or six,
> Over the moon-touched cobbles
> Past still shadowed houses,
> Up ever till the top came
> And there her quiet house was,
> Moon-touched like the cobbles;
> Nearer heaven.
>
> He stood there, heart running
> From the long, expectant climb.
> Hope beat upon hope
> In the tired-imaged brain.
> The remote, star-softened sea
> Healed hurt with another hurt,
> And he stayed a long minute.
>
> Once a man passed – strangely
> Before he sighed and went
> Down the seven hills, or six,
> Over the moon-touched cobbles,
> Aching for want of speech.

During those carefree seaside holidays at the start of the Forties, Eamonn, who was, after all, preoccupied with his own thoughts on life and love, took little interest in the momentous events then taking place on the other side of the Irish Sea. Although one morning in January 1941 a German plane, on its way back from a raid on Belfast, unloaded its remaining bombs on Dublin and killed thirty people, it was an isolated incident and the war in Europe scarcely touched him.

The fact that he spent the war in neutral Ireland was to have an effect on him years later, however, in his television career, especially when he was presenting 'This Is Your Life'. By its very nature that programme featured numerous war heroes but because of the comparatively sheltered and safe life he had lived throughout the war it was practically impossible for him to empathise with them. The fact that so many were 'officer class' made the boy from an Irish working class background even more ill at ease.

Most of his little knowledge of the war he had garnered from cinema newsreels and Hollywood-made war films. Consequently it became an endless struggle for his programme teams, both at the BBC and, years later, at Thames TV, to convince him that 'lieutenant' was not pronounced 'lootenant'. Despite all their efforts however he seemed incapable of believing the word was 'leftenant' and, thirty years later, he was still embarrassing his 'This Is Your Life' colleagues by addressing Lieutenant-Generals and Lieutenant-Commanders as 'Lootenant-Generals' and 'Lootenant-Commanders'.

It may have created problems with Eamonn's pronunciation but, in fact, the war has given longer life to the British version of 'This Is Your Life' because even many years after it had been over a subject's good war record has been 'the peg' on which to hang a programme.

Many non-celebrity subjects have also been people whose work place is the sea, lifeboatmen, coastguards and Air-Sea-Rescue personnel, and the production team believe that fact has also helped to give the programme much more staying power than the original American version.

They are convinced that if it was not being produced on an island that had also been involved in a world war it would not have run for half as long.

At the time those bombs fell on Dublin, Eamonn was still in his first year at the Hibernian Insurance company, but his thoughts were concentrated more and more on how he could break into broadcasting.

Later that year he finally did get the chance of his first broadcast. And, as it happened, it was not a boxing commentary.

Every Saturday evening, Radio Eireann put out a ten minute sports bulletin which was broadcast by a Dublin table tennis player, Harry Carlile. One weekend early in 1941, Harry was selected to play in an international match and the shoestring-run station told him to find somebody himself to take his place for that Saturday's broadcast.

Rooting through a file of job applications he came across Eamonn's request for an audition, with its emphasis on his elocution lessons, listened to a recording of his commentary, and offered him the job.

Eamonn was no stranger to Radio Eireann's building and knew most of the few programme people employed there. He had been there twice before, once with a friend for an interview as a would-be contestant on a school quiz programme, which he failed, and the second time to discuss his audition for the job of boxing commentator.

Even so, he found the conditions in the studio, in which old blankets were used to make it – almost – soundproof, rather primitive. But he was elated by the feeling he got from broadcasting those few brief sports reports. Here he was speaking to thousands of people he did not know but without any of the blushing he suffered when he encountered strangers face to face. Or, much worse, the feeling at those moments that he was about to be physically and embarrassingly sick, which he was now beginning to get.

Many years later, when he no longer suffered from the problem, except only occasionally and in the mildest degree, and he was able to talk about it, Eamonn told me how he felt when that happened.

'It was totally inexplicable,' he said. 'As I was meeting somebody for the first time, either one person or a number of them, a voice inside me would suddenly say, "This would be a terrible time, a most dreadfully embarrassing time, to be sick ... to vomit." And immediately I would start to retch.

'It was something I just could not control. I could not explain it to myself and so there was no possible way I could expect the people in whose company it happened to understand it. I felt they would consider it totally unforgivable because it seemed I was not saying but actually demonstrating that they made me feel sick.'

But there was no such feeling the day he made that first broadcast. There was just him and a microphone.

However, to Eamonn's disappointment Harry the table tennis player was not called on to take up his bat for his country again and he had to wait nearly another year for his next broadcast. This time it was a boxing commentary.

It was in November 1941, a month before his nineteenth birthday, that Radio Eireann invited him to commentate on some of the semi-final bouts in the Irish Junior National Amateur Boxing Championships, taking the place of the usual commentator while he was out gargling with Guinness to prepare his throat for the finals.

There was, however, one little complication for Eamonn. He was boxing in the same competition.

After he had thought it over, however, he chose not to bring that fact to Radio Eireann's attention. They would have had little choice but to replace him. They could scarcely risk the possibility that when it came time for their commentator to be describing a fight for their listeners he was, at worst, being counted out in the ring or, at best, bleeding all over their microphone from a busted nose.

As for Eamonn, he had every confidence – he told himself – that he would be eliminated in one of the preliminary bouts long before finals day.

But he won them all and qualified to fight on the big day itself – in a semi-final on which he was supposed to be commentating.

He realised that the only way out of the dilemma was to make a deal with the commentator he was relieving. So, in exchange for an offer of free Guinness, Radio Eireann's man agreed to commentate on the semi-final in which Eamonn was boxing before going off for his break.

Although his mind was as much, if not more, on his debut as a commentator as it was on his opponent, Eamonn got the decision in that fight, too. Then, to the crowd's astonishment, he leapt out of the ring, gathered up the clothing he had left at the ringside and bounded up to the radio control-box at the back of the stadium from where, still in singlet and shorts, he gave a breathless commentary on the next fight before pulling on his clothes and commentating on the two fights after that.

And, later, with the regular commentator back in the box, he returned to the ring to fight in his final and become Junior

Middleweight Champion of Ireland.

Radio Eireann decided he had proved his ability as a commentator, too.

During the fights leading up to the final, Eamonn had been well supported by his friends at the insurance company where he had now been promoted from clerk to the sales staff. But when he went into the office on the morning after a fight his face would still be bearing the scars of the contest and it was mentioned to him that a salesman with a broken nose or a cauliflower ear did not have the best face to present to would-be buyers of insurance.

His father had never been enthusiastic about his boxing, although he was understandably proud when he won the championship, and his mother had always refused to watch him fight. Now Willie said it was time for him to give it up. Any thoughts of his son becoming a professional boxer were out of the question. That's not what a School Leaving Certificate and elocution lessons were for. Now that he had the title, Eamonn also agreed it was a sensible time to quit.

Eamonn claimed that from that day on he never lifted a fist to anyone. But, from the mid-Seventies to the day he died, a rumour circulated throughout Ireland that he once knocked out an Irish politician, who was later to become the country's Prime Minister, at a reception in the city's Shelbourne Hotel.

According to the story, Eamonn and Charles Haughey had heated words during which Eamonn punched Haughey and he lost consciousness.

The story circulated so widely that a national Sunday newspaper was emboldened to print it as a true story in 1979. However, Eamonn sued and got a public apology from them in the High Court, together with damages and costs. Even after that, however, the story still persisted.

The events at the National Stadium proved to be even more important in the shaping of the future Eamonn Andrews than the somewhat remarkable fact that he both won a national boxing championship and broadcast a boxing commentary on the same night.

The tremendous personal acclaim he earned by these accomplishments together with the realisation they were each of his own making, gave him the confidence to start disregarding the dictates of his father, on whom he could now look down both from a point of view of height and of achievement.

Once he had quit the boxing ring it did not take him long to find himself another arena in which he would be the centre of attraction. The new Junior Middleweight Champion of Ireland, who, on the strength of that first brief sports bulletin before the boxing commentary and one newspaper article, was already carrying printed business cards announcing himself as 'Eamonn Andrews, Commentator and Journalist', simply started his own amateur dramatic company.

Had he merely been keen on acting he could have joined the society in the local church hall to which his father belonged. But he was not interested in the minor parts a newcomer would be offered there. With his own company he could cast himself, as he very soon did, in such meaty leading roles as Danny, the murderous psychopath in 'Night Must Fall'. And no little church hall for him, either. His stage was usually the one in Dublin Town Hall, no less.

His next venture was even more ambitious. He decided he would make his start as a playwright and, when he had written the play, produce it himself at the professional Peacock Theatre, right next door to the prestigious Abbey, and also play the leading role.

The play, a three act drama set in Dublin, was based on an Irish folk poem about a consumptive artist who strangles his mistress with her own long tresses because he cannot bear to see her beauty fade – except that, for the sake of decency, Eamonn made the artist and mistress man and wife. He gave this epic the dramatic but implausible title 'The Moon Is Black'.

Unfortunately the play's future was not very bright either.

It was not surprising, however. The portents were never good. Because Eamonn tackled the business of writing a play rather like he had the job of filing clerk.

First of all, he booked the theatre before he had written a single word of it. So, with his father directing, the cast had to go into rehearsal as soon as Eamonn had finished the first act. But at that time neither the company nor his father had any idea what the second act was going to be about. Worse than that, neither did Eamonn, and he was supposed to be writing it.

Then, when he finally finished writing the play, he discovered it was at least half an hour shorter than the normal running time and he had to keep on writing new scenes to pad it out.

Finally it was finished – and staged. But it was not very well received.

However, as, for just one thing, its leading character, who was supposed to be a puny little, tuberculosis-ridden painter, was being played by the super-fit, barrel-chested, six-feet-tall, Junior Middleweight Boxing Champion of Ireland, this was perhaps understandable.

The critics panned both the play and its leading player, and for the two weeks of its run the theatre's box office became the loneliest spot in Dublin. As he peeped from the wings to 'count the house' each night and realised there would yet again be fewer people in the audience than on the stage, Eamonn the pragmatist gradually came to the conclusion he would make as little from writing plays as he had from writing poetry. So, sensibly, he rang down the curtain on that particular ambition and decided he must look elsewhere to satisfy the thirst for fame he had now acquired.

3

The 'Question Time'
mystery and a
touch of blackmail

The embarrassing failure of the play persuaded Eamonn that, for the present at any rate, he should confine his aspirations for fame to the business of commentating.

He soon realised, however, that there was a snag to that. Boxing contests in Ireland that were of sufficient importance to interest Radio Eireann were very few and it was clear that if he confined his commentating to that sport alone he would get little in the way of broadcasting experience and scarcely any cash to supplement his earnings from the insurance company.

So, although boxing was the only sport of which he had any real knowledge, he decided to try to get commentary work on others.

First he persuaded Radio Eireann to give him a test commentary on a horse race. During the week before, he made a list of the names of the horses, checked their correct pronunciations and started to memorise them. But, as he knew each horse carried a large number on its saddlecloth, he did not bother to familiarise himself with the jockey's colours.

The commentary was to be of a race over the jumps at Baldoyle Racecourse, and he was to talk into a microphone positioned on the ledge in the open commentary box in the stand which would carry his commentary down the line to Radio Eireann's studios for the benefit of listening executives who would judge his performance.

But, almost as soon as the race had started and he had begun his commentary, the wind began to whip up the horses numbered cloths. By then the horses were already rounding a bend and racing down the far side of the course. All he could see were the colours on the jockey's caps.

So in near panic, he began to describe a completely fictitious race in which he mentioned the names of the horses on his list but in any order that came to mind.

Despite all, he still managed to make the race sound exciting and probably convincing enough. But these were the days before the lip-microphone and listeners could hear the sounds from outside the commentary box as well as from inside.

Eamonn had just described the end of the race, enthusiastically punching out the name of his imagined winner, followed by his selected second and third, when a punter standing just outside the box lowered his field glasses, and turned to glare at him. Then he called out in a loud, clear voice, 'You've got the wrong bloody horse. That one fell two fences back and the ones you said were second and third were way down the field.'

Eamonn never heard what the executives of Radio Eireann thought of his potential as a racing commentator and he did not think it wise to ask them.

Next he turned to cricket. It was, however, very much a minority sport in which the radio station had no interest. So as a self-pro-claimed 'Broadcaster and Journalist' he did the next best thing and got an Irish newspaper to commission him to report a match. But he totally ignored the bowling averages, of which he had no knowledge anyway, failed to distinguish between professional and amateur players, which was of some importance at that time, left before the end, and padded out his report by writing an essay on the weather which deserved to win him yet another bicycle.

Then he tried soccer. And immediately he scored an own goal that got him the sack from his job at the insurance company.

In response to Eamonn's badgering, Radio Eireann agreed to let him share the commentary on a game between English and Irish Football League teams in Dublin with a staff broadcaster, and his boss at the insurance company gave him the afternoon off.

Then he learned the English side had another match in Belfast a few days before they were to play in Dublin. So, because he was desperate to learn something about the two teams, and about the game itself for that matter, he asked for another day off to go to

Belfast to see it. But this time his boss refused.

So Eamonn got his young sister, Kathleen, to phone the firm to say he was ill.

But he did not tell the other commentator about the fib and during the commentary of the match in Dublin the Radio Eireann staffman suddenly said, 'Well Eamonn, I think you'd agree the English are not playing as well as they did when we watched them in Belfast.' With sinking heart, Eamonn had to come in and confirm this observation.

Next morning his boss, who had been listening, called him to his office and gave him an ultimatum – insurance or broadcasting. Eamonn, expecting it, said it had to be broadcasting and handed in his notice.

However, it was not quite the bold decision it might have seemed because by then he was being paid two guineas a week to write a radio column for the Irish Independent – later he was to become a columnist for the London evening paper *The Star* and for the *Catholic Herald* – and he had become very friendly with a young producer at Radio Eireann. Very soon he was to get his first big break on a show that friend produced.

Each summer the Irish Tourist Board sponsored a quiz-show, 'Question Time', which was broadcast from the country's holiday resorts and compered by a part-time broadcaster who was also a barrister.

The barrister was very politically orientated, however, and at a public meeting following the death of a man who had died in prison after being jailed for subversive activities he accused the Irish government of being 'Belsen camp gaolers'.

This caused an uproar in the Irish Parliament and the Tourist Board was forced to pay him off. The job was then offered to two more broadcasters but they turned it down. Then it was offered to Eamonn, who was far from politically orientated, and, quickly accepted it.

It was that programme that provided him with his first regular work in broadcasting and was the all-important job that took him from occasional boxing commentaries to programmes proper. Strangely, however, when, less than twenty years later, he wrote his autobiography he did not even give it a passing mention.

To get to the resorts for the programme recordings, Eamonn

bought an old open-topped MG tourer and almost immediately nearly killed himself, and two friends, in it.

To celebrate his acquisition of both the programme and the car he drove out to a golf club at Howth which he had got to know during his summers at the chalet.

Out of sight of his critical and abstemious father, he had now developed a taste for beer, Smithwicks light ale with a dash of lime juice, and he drank rather a lot of it that night.

As he drove down a steep hill on the return journey in the early hours of the following morning, the car went off the road and overturned into a ditch. But, because the hood was down, all three were thrown clear and none was badly hurt. Between them they managed to manhandle the car back on to the road again and continue their journey.

Eamonn was a success on 'Question Time' and also when, in a sponsored programme for a Dublin cleaning company, he became half of a radio double act with the resounding names of 'Stainless and Spotless'. But he was rather less successful when he tried to be a disc jockey on a programme sponsored by Kavanagh's, a food firm whose sales pitch was: 'The makers of pure food products'. On the day of the first broadcast he opened the show with the line: 'This programme is brought to you by Kavanagh's – the makers of *poor* food products'.

He was forgiven, however, and shortly afterwards was given his first ever interview programme, 'Microphone Parade', a copy of the BBC radio's 'In Town Tonight' in which he talked to celebrities visiting Dublin. He was now established as a regular Radio Eireann broadcaster.

But he had ambitions to be seen as well as heard; despite the failure of 'The Moon Is Black!' he still hankered after success on the stage.

So he joined the Gaiety School of Acting which was directed by Ria Mooney, a former Abbey Theatre actress who, years before, had created the role of Rosie Redmond in Sean O'Casey's controversial play 'The Plough and the Stars'.

Shortly afterwards he was given the chance to appear in a one-act curtain raiser preceding the play then in production at the theatre, during rehearsals for which he was to discover that, despite his elocution lessons, he was occasionally still sliding into a thick

Dublin accent with one or two words.

The script called for him to shout for a cushion for a female character who was feeling faint. However, when he did so, he pronounced it 'kes-shunn'. Miss Mooney shouted the correct pronunciation at him, and kept shouting, every time he got it wrong – which was frequently.

By the end of the dress rehearsal Eamonn finally had it right. However, as a further safeguard, when the performance proper started he stood in the wings repeating it over and over as he waited for his cue. Finally he was on stage and when the female character announced that she felt faint he called confidently and immaculately for a cushion.

But the rest of the cast, all newcomers like himself, gaped at him in startled amazement. Because at that point in the play he should have been calling for a glass of water for the fainting lady. The request for a cushion came four pages later.

At the end of that first term, Miss Mooney told a disappointed Eamonn he was not going to make it as an actor. It had nothing to do with his problem pronouncing words like cushion, however. It was, she told him, because he had 'an incurable monotone' in his voice.

Equally incurable was the love Eamonn now had of dressing up in theatrical costumes. It was a predilection he was to find an excuse to express years later on 'This Is Your Life'.

The excuse for the elaborate outfits he donned at the beginning of most of those programmes was that they were disguises to enable him to get to the subject and spring his surprise without being detected. But, in truth, the costumes he wore – anything from a pantomime Humpty Dumpty to 'surprise' comedian Arthur Askey to an Arab sheik, complete with camel, for 'Coronation Street' actor William Roache – were so preposterous they frequently drew more attention to him rather than less.

And during his last few seasons presenting the show the reasons for his choice of some of those costumes had become quite implausible.

One of the last celebrities he surprised was Virgin Records boss, Richard Branson. Eamonn decided he would confront him dressed as Long John Silver, complete with a parrot on his shoulder. Why? Simple. At that time Branson lived on a boat. To point out that it was a luxurious houseboat, with all mod cons, and was moored on a fashionable stretch of a London canal, was simply splitting hairs, and risking his wrath.

Not only did Eamonn keep up his delusions about acting in that vicarious way, twenty years after he had been told he would not make it on the stage he went back to the Gaiety Theatre – because one of his companies had taken it over. (And another twenty years later he lost control of it again when his Irish entertainments empire collapsed.)

When the Gaiety school told Eamonn they saw little future for him there he turned his attention to the variety stage. And for someone who could not sing, dance or even tell jokes with any confidence of remembering the ending, he could not have chosen a more fortuitous moment.

At that time, the Irish Government required cinema owners to pay less entertainment tax if they put on live shows as well as imported films, which was not meant to imply that live shows would be less entertaining, only that they would be employing more local labour. One cinema chain reckoned that, along with one or two music hall acts, a quiz show with members of the audience as contestants, would qualify them for the concession. And they were right. Compared with some of the cinemas in Ireland, a quiz show was a major production. Some provincial ones settled for little more than a tone-deaf pianist battering an ancient upright piano.

Dublin's 2,000 seater Theatre Royal had tried out a nightly quiz show, 'Double or Nothing', in which contestants were asked up to four questions. They won 2/6d for answering the first question correctly and were entitled to take the money or risk losing or doubling it with the next, and so on to the top prize of one whole pound.

The quiz proved to be such a success that the Theatre Royal owners decided to introduce it to other cinemas in their chain. Eamonn auditioned and although he looked, and clearly felt, very ill at ease, his growing reputation as a broadcaster got him the job of quizmaster at a cinema in Limerick.

He was already very familiar with the Theatre Royal when he went for the audition because it was from there that he had commentated on his first professional boxing match while he was still working for the insurance company.

It was for the Irish Heavyweight Championship. The ring had

been erected on the stage and commentary box high up in the wings.

The winner was a boxer named Martin Thornton and a few months later, shortly after the end of the war, fight promoter Jack Solomons brought over the British champion, Bruce Woodcock, for a match with him. Thornton did not relish a meeting with the highly reputed Woodcock but the £800 purse was too much to resist.

Besides making the commentary Radio Eireann wanted Eamonn to get a comment from Thornton after the fight, win or lose, and come back on the air with it later in the evening. He had done this after the previous fight, too, and he had not liked the perilous climb up and down the steel ladder by which the commentary box was reached. So, not relishing having to make the climb again, he visited Thornton in his dressing room before the start of the fight, and asked him for a comment he could attribute to him when the fight was over.

Thornton thought for a moment and said, 'Tell them I said I am sorry but I did my best.' Eamonn was about to point out that the fight had not even started yet. But he saw the despairing look in the boxer's eyes and decided not to bother.

The fight was only a few minutes old before Eamonn knew the comment Thornton had given him in advance would be more than adequate. Thornton was so badly outclassed by Woodcock that many of the spectators clearly felt that for him to say he was doing his best was something of an exaggeration.

To carry out the job of quiz show presenter and also keep on with his radio work Eamonn had to drive to Limerick and back every day, a round trip of nearly 250 miles, and on one of the very first of these journeys he was again in an accident.

He was driving through a small market town on his way to Limerick on a winter's day when the car skidded into a kerb, the driver's door fell off and Eamonn was thrown out. But again he escaped serious injury as he went skidding along the roadway on his backside. From there he watched the driverless car continue on down the High Street until it crashed into the wall of the local policeman's house, cracking a drainpipe.

The enraged policeman came storming out but quickly calmed down when Eamonn offered him money both to compensate for the fractured pipe and to forget about the whole incident. The policeman eventually settled for thirty shillings.

Eamonn then threw the door on to the back seat and started on his journey again. But the moment he sat behind the wheel and his backside came into contact with the cold leather upholstery he realised that as he skidded along the road he had lost the seat of his trousers.

Unfortunately, it was the only suit he had. Later that night, as his introductory music was played on the organ, he stepped out before the audience in that hot, little cinema with all the dignity he could muster – wearing his heavy black overcoat.

Soon afterwards, Eddie Byrne, an actor who was question master of the quiz in Dublin, was offered film work in England and Eamonn was given the job at the Theatre Royal where they prided themselves with putting much more zing into the production than was the case in the provinces.

There Eamonn did not just step on to the stage to the sound of a mere electric organ. With a full orchestra playing he was swept out at the centre of a line of chorus girls who were singing the roistering couplet:

'If it's "Double or Nothing" you're waiting for,
'Then Eamonn's here to give you some more!'

He never experienced anything like the embarrassment of having to conceal ripped trousers in the time he was at the Theatre Royal, but at first he thought nothing of wearing the white socks his mother knitted him with his dinner suit and black patent-leather shoes – until one night the horrified theatre manager sent him back to his dressing-room to change them. His excuse that he was colour blind cut no ice, he was told he would never be allowed on stage dressed like that again. The embarrassment of that lesson from then on made him very sensitive about criticism of his dress sense.

His wife, Grainne, later said that when they were married she told him, 'Give me £50 and I'll get you well dressed.' To which she added, 'It was then that people started to take him more seriously.'

But, despite that, Eamonn had several more sartorial setbacks in his career. After the wedding he started to wear a gold ring on the third finger of his left hand.

Shortly afterwards, Gilbert Harding, the famous cantankerous 'What's My Line?' panellist, told him that a man wearing a ring on 'the engagement finger' was betraying a 'lack of breeding'. If he must wear a ring at all, he said, it should be on the little finger.

As soon as Harding was out of sight, Eamonn whipped the ring off and, to be on the safe side, never again wore a ring on *any* finger.

During the second of the chat shows which brought him to commercial television one of the guests, comedian Ted Ray, mischievously stretched out his hand and twanged the braces Eamonn was wearing. Then he leaned forward and for the benefit of millions of ITV viewers read aloud something that was printed on them. 'Property of the BBC', it said.

After that night Eamonn stopped wearing not only the braces he had brought with him from the BBC but any braces at all. From then on he always wore a belt. (Ray shook him on another occasion when Eamonn introduced him to actor Roger Moore, just before he became the screen James Bond, and Ray said to him, 'Roger Moore? Oh, is that your name or your ambition?')

During another edition of 'The 'Eamonn Andrews Show', actress Sandra Gough, who then played Irma Ogden in Coronation Street, playfully slipped her hand inside his shirt. But she withdrew it instantly, saying 'Oh, Eamonn, you're wearing a string vest! I think string vests are a real turn-off!'. Not a man to take chances, after that Eamonn did not ever again wear a vest of any kind.

After his lesson from the theatre manager in Dublin he naturally took some trouble to try to get it all right for his very first appearance on television. So when millions of viewers got their first ever glimpse of the BBC's bright new radio star in 1951 they saw a carefully groomed man who was dressed immaculately in a new, expensively tailored dress suit, crisp white shirt, and shiny patent-leather shoes. One thing was puzzling, though. He was not wearing a tie.

Eamonn had just finished the out-of-vision commentary on a televised boxing match when, as prearranged, he climbed into the ring to interview the winner. But, as he bent down to duck under the ropes, his clip-on bow tie went flying off across the ring and under the feet of the boxers, and trainers, managers and hangers-on who had climbed in, and he had to conduct the interview without it. After that he learned how to tie one.

He had not long been presenting 'Double or Nothing' at the Dublin cinema before he decided the real place to be was not on the stage but right up there on the big silver screen.

So, in a summer break from the show, and disregarding his total lack of achievement at acting school, he set off for England optimistically hoping his looks and physique alone would make him a matinee idol. He tried every one of the then numerous film studios but found not a single producer who felt the same way.

He went back to Dublin and the quiz show.

Shortly afterwards, however, the Joe Loss Orchestra was booked for two weeks at the Theatre Royal and when he saw 'Double Or Nothing' the band leader thought it would be worth introducing into his own touring band show when he returned to England. He liked Eamonn, too, because – as he said later – he was very much like himself, somewhat strait-laced, seemingly not promiscuous and (at that time) fairly abstemious. So he invited him to join him.

Eamonn agreed, settled for a salary of £50 a week, and had his first introduction to British audiences in 1950 at London's Finsbury Park Empire, where the three-month tour opened. On the bill also was a new young comedian named Spike Milligan.

Before the tour came to an end Joe Loss suggested to the BBC that they should engage Eamonn to introduce a series of broadcasts the orchestra was about to make. But they wrote back saying they did not think he would add anything worthwhile to the proposed programmes.

Eamonn, who had sent the BBC tapes of his Radio Eireann broadcasts, also made a personal approach to the Outside Broadcast Department. He got an interview and was given a voice test, followed by the encouraging news that it was 'suitable' for the BBC.

The Head of Outside Broadcasts also listened to his most recent boxing commentaries. But he told Eamonn that even if they could use him they would not consider paying his fare over from his home in Dublin, and his expenses, on top of the £15 fee, just for one commentary.

Eamonn pleaded that he would pay his own way purely for the opportunity but the H.O.B., as the BBC, with its love of initials, styled him, said it would be out of the question.

However, Eamonn had only been back home for a couple of months, and starting to pick up freelance radio work again, when he saw a newspaper report that the BBC boxing commentator Stewart MacPherson was returning to his native Canada.

Immediately he applied for the job. To his delight a letter arrived at the little council house where he still lived, with his parents, brother and sisters, offering him an audition.

However, to his surprise, it was not to try him out as a boxing commentator but for another of MacPherson's broadcasting jobs, chairing a programme called 'Ignorance Is Bliss' which had already been running intermittently for four years, and which the BBC was bringing back for another three-month run. The programme was a cod quiz show in which a panel of comedians tried to get laughs from the audience rather than come up with correct answers to the deliberately moronic questions.

The letter informed Eamonn the auditions would be held in the Aeolian Hall, then used as the headquarters of the BBC's Variety Department, in London's Bond Street, on a Sunday morning.

Excited though he was, he was also so nervous about how to pronounce Aeolian that he actually wrote out the whole address in capitals before he left home. Then, after travelling to London by boat and train, he handed the note to a taxi driver at Euston station like a non-English-speaking tourist.

Even before the audition Eamonn had already met two of the three 'Ignorance Is Bliss' panellists when they had appeared in variety at the Theatre Royal, Harold Berens, who played a fast-talking, Cockney spiv character and monocle-wearing Michael Moore, who aped an upper crust Englishman.

Years later, after Eamonn had become a success on television, Berens claimed he had been the one who had recommended him for the job with the programme when he heard McPherson was planning to leave. If that was the case then Eamonn was not very grateful, because, despite a bombardment of telephone calls and letters, he remained deaf to all appeals from the then almost forgotten Berens for a spot on his chat show. Nor, for that matter, did he ever invite the other panellists, Michael Moore and Gladys Hay, the daughter of the celebrated comedian, Will Hay.

The truth seemed to be that, as soon as he became established with such successes as 'What's My Line?' and 'This Is Your Life', Eamonn, probably wisely, decided that his beginnings with 'that nonsense show', as he then called it, should be forgotten as soon as possible.

While Berens was insisting he was responsible for Eamonn getting the audition, Gladys Hay claimed it was her who saved him from making a failure of it.

She was a buxom lady of sixteen stones and, as such, was the butt of many of the scripted lines in the series. But, according to her memory of it, when the audition script called for Eamonn to insult her he was not able to do so; he became almost speechless with embarrassment.

So, according to her later claim, when the producer announced a break to give Eamonn a chance to compose himself, she took him on one side and gave him a pep talk about the chance he was ruining while also reassuring him her feelings would not be hurt by the things the script called on him to say.

Despite whatever help he might have had from Miss Hay, Eamonn was very pessimistic about his performance at the audition but, afterwards, was intrigued when he was approached by the man who held the British rights to the programme, Maurice Winnick, who suggested a confidential chat.

At first Eamonn was flattered because Winnick was one of the best known names in broadcasting – in immediate postwar British broadcasting one of the most often repeated lines among the credits after radio programmes was 'By arrangement with Maurice Winnick'.

When the war broke out he had been a band leader, and throughout it he had continued to play at British and American troop concerts in England and Europe with both British and American bandsmen.

With the Americans he listened on VHF radio to their favourite radio shows, saw the potential of some of them for postwar British radio and, immediately hostilities ceased, acquired the European rights to a number of them. These he then licensed to the BBC.

At the start of their chat, Winnick cheered Eamonn considerably when he told him that despite his fears he had done 'quite well' at the audition.

But he then went on to make it clear that, such was his influence, only a hopeful who signed a personal contract with him would get the job. That meant he would be taking a percentage of the successful aspirant's earnings, both from radio and from the even more lucrative touring stage version that was planned.

Eamonn, sensing this was blackmail, managed to remain non-committal. He thought Winnick might be bluffing about the amount of influence he could wield with the mighty BBC. He said he would think it over.

Back home in Dublin, where his father was now in failing health and had not been able to work for a year, he began to think it over more and more as the weeks passed and no word came from the BBC. Winnick meantime phoned frequently to ask him for his decision. Eventually Eamonn received a telegram from him asking him to return to London for an urgent meeting. Eamonn decided he had better go.

The meeting was in the evening at Winnick's luxuriously appointed apartment in London's Park Lane. The former band leader, who was never very subtle, was even more direct than he had been at their first meeting. He put a contract on the coffee table and told the already perspiring Eamonn that if he signed it he would get the job. If he refused, the job would go to somebody else. It was as uncomplicated as that.

Eamonn still hesitated. He hated the thought of being beholden to such an unscrupulous man as this. But as Winnick painted the picture of the glittering, lucrative career that lay ahead if he did sign, and compared it with the prospect of returning to Dublin empty handed, Eamonn's mental moral stance started to weaken. Eventually he signed.

He left Winnick's flat in the early hours of the morning and walked into Hyde Park where, in a spasm of self-loathing, he was suddenly and violently sick. A few days afterwards the BBC announced that he was to be the new presenter of 'Ignorance Is Bliss' and his voice was heard on BBC radio for the first time ever a couple of weeks later, on February 20, 1950.

The following month he returned to Dublin for the funeral of his father and flew back the same day for another edition of the programme.

Soon the name of Eamonn Andrews was better known in Britain than it was in Ireland. Oddly, however, if Winnick had got his way on another occasion the name would never have been heard of outside Ireland at all. But an Irishman with the unlikely name of Bob Jones might have been.

In the weeks before the start of his job with 'Ignorance Is Bliss' Winnick told Eamonn he was worried English audiences would not be able to pronounce his name. He suggested he should drop Eamonn and call himself 'something reliable and homely, like Bob'.

And, as there was already a broadcaster named Bob Andrews

at the time, Winnick also suggested Eamonn should go a step further with the 'homely touch' and call himself plain Bob Jones.

Fortunately Eamonn was able to resist Winnick that time, though, years later, Hollywood star Jon Voight appeared to endorse the agent's opinion when he was filming a tribute for the 'This Is Your Life' of John Schlesinger, who had directed him in the Oscar-winning 'Midnight Cowboy'.

It suited Eamonn's ego to give the impression he was so big in international celebrity circles that all the international names who took part in his shows were personal friends, so he insisted that when they made a film contribution they should be asked to start by addressing him by name, before speaking to the 'guest of honour'.

When the production team looked at the piece Voight filmed for Schlesinger before inserting it in the show, they found he had started by saying, 'Hello Eamonn ... Eamonn? Eamonn? What the fuck sort of name is Eamonn?' The line was, of course, deleted before the film was edited into the programme for transmission.

Although the press publicity he got at the time was kind to him, Eamonn received no other programme offers during the run of 'Ignorance Is Bliss' and when it came to an end he was out of a job.

Home for him then was a basement flat in Bayswater owned by the mother of its other occupant, a West End stage manager to whom he had been introduced through mutual Irish friends.

As he had with his childhood in Dublin, Eamonn afterwards romanticised the hardships he endured during that brief spell of unemployment. He used to claim that his diet consisted almost exclusively of Irish stew, a saucepan of which he kept permanently on the stove, occasionally replenishing it with vegetables but very seldom with meat. He also spoke of what a big treat it was when copies of the Irish newspapers arrived in the post – because his mother concealed slices of bacon wrapped in greaseproof paper between the pages.

It was true his mother smuggled bacon into Britain for him by that bizarre channel, but only to supplement the stringent meat rationing which still existed.

There was never the slightest fear Eamonn would suffer the kind of deprivation that would reduce him to anything approaching the proportions with which he could convincingly portray the tragic hero of 'The Moon Is Black!'

4

Luck on the 'Line'
and a date
with a dancer

Despite his remembered poverty, Eamonn still had enough money with which to pay his way at one of the BBC staff's favourite locals, the Cock Tavern, close to Broadcasting House. It was at the bar there one lunch time that another Irish friend, Brian George, who was Head of Recorded Programmes at the BBC, introduced him to a Scots sporting journalist named Angus McKay.

McKay was editor of BBC radio's long-running 'Sport's Report', and was on the lookout for a new presenter. He had heard Eamonn on 'Ignorance Is Bliss' and had been very much taken with his voice.

However, it was not a programme that appealed to his dour Scot's nature and he had presumed that to have become involved with it Eamonn must have been a very lightweight performer. But when he read a newspaper report that he had been an amateur boxer his interest in him increased. During the conversation that followed that meeting he invited Eamonn to visit the 'Sport's Report' studio while the programme was on the air and, afterwards, asked him if he would like to have a trial as a presenter by introducing the much briefer version of it which went out on the BBC Overseas Service.

Eamonn readily agreed and McKay was so pleased with his performance that, immediately afterwards, he offered him the presenter's job on the main 'Sport's Report' programme itself. Eamonn accepted gratefully. He realised that the programme was to give him a firm foothold at the BBC at last.

His job on it was not only to introduce the programme and link all of its many items with the help of a prepared script but also to interview sporting personalities and to chair discussions.

However, McKay was soon to discover Eamonn was not the ideal man for the vital interviewing part of the job; his new frontman had nothing like the knowledge of sport, or even the interest in it, he had presumed him to have. In fact, he knew little or nothing about any sport other than boxing.

With this realisation came another – he had to find a solution to the problem.

One obvious one was to pass on to Eamonn his own vast knowledge of sport. And that was exactly what he decided to do. Not all at once, which would have been impossible, but at the precise times Eamonn needed it.

So every Saturday afternoon as Eamonn interviewed the sporting personalities, McKay talked quietly into a microphone in the control room on the other side of a glass partition and Eamonn listened to him on his earpiece.

By this method McKay told Eamonn what to ask, when to change the subject, how to reply when the interviewee turned the tables and put a question to him instead. In fact, in this way he orchestrated whole interviews, even studio discussions.

The questions were McKay's, the voice was Eamonn's. The combination worked immediately and worked so well that the radio-linked double act lasted for thirteen years until Eamonn lost favour with the BBC and moved to ITV.

Soon after he had joined 'Sport's Report', and again thanks to his friend Brian George, he was offered two more radio programmes on which he played records and interviewed immigrants and tourists, 'Welcome to Britain' and 'Welcome Stranger'. And as a result of those he was put on the rota of presenters of 'Housewives' Choice' with a three week contract which was to be repeated many times throughout the next decade.

When he started to introduce 'Housewives' Choice' he decided the way the breakfast-time show would make his a household name was to use it to put a catchphrase on the nation's lips.

So, as a starting point, he took the Irish greeting 'Top Of The Morning!' – which, in fact, owed more to Music Halls than to Tara's

Halls – and eventually came up with the line, 'Hello. it's tip-top – and it's top of the morning!'

Eamonn was very pleased, but the housewives were merely puzzled. As he punched his snappy catch-phrase at them first thing each morning they just carried on yawning.

So eventually, he settled for the English translation of a more genuine Gaelic greeting, which he did not bastardise, 'A Hundred Thousand Welcomes', which left the nation unmoved to a man, but at least not mystified.

What he did not realise was that with a voice as distinct as his, he did not need to rely on catchphrases, any way, and despite Maurice Winnick's misgivings the name of Eamonn Andrews was soon becoming one of the best known in Britain.

Not long afterwards his face, too, was to become equally well known, thanks to yet another Irishman, this time a fellow Dubliner who had even been a member of the same boxing club as Eamonn, though not at the same time. He was a BBC producer named T. Leslie Jackson who in the spring of 1951 had been given the job of launching the successful American panel show, 'What's My Line?', another programme to which Winnick had the European rights.

The BBC had been searching for a successful television panel game for five years but none they had tried had worked. The first in 1946 had the same basic idea as 'What's My Line?'. It was called 'What's In A Face?' and in it the panel tried to guess the contestant's occupation from his or her face.

Then came 'Play The Game', the programme in which Gilbert Harding made his first television appearance; 'Crossword', a complicated crossword puzzle programme with visual and verbal clues; and 'We Beg To Differ' a successful radio show which did not work as well on television.

While the BBC were struggling to find the right panel game format, the shrewd Mr Winnick had taken another trip to America. There he had seen the brand-new and immediately successful 'What's My Line?', had acquired the European rights of that show, too, and then offered it to the BBC.

In the days of live television, before video tape, programmes were recorded for later viewing, or for syndication, by training a film camera on a television screen while the programme was being transmitted. The resultant film was called a kinescope and Winnick brought back with him one of 'What's My Line?' to show the BBC.

As now, all American shows were sponsored. That itself was something for which, burdened as they were with the dogma of their first director general, the solemn, puritanical, Lord Reith, that the BBC's sole purpose was to be an unequivocal communicator, the eminences grises at 'Auntie Beeb' were still ill-prepared.

But when they looked at the kinescope of 'What's My Line?', which was sponsored by a firm of deodorant manufacturers, they practically reached for their own nosegays.

For the messages the sponsor's spokesman delivered at the beginning, middle and end of the programme were the instructional, 'Puff! and away goes perspiration!'; the poetical, 'Make the armpit the charm-pit'; and the meteorological, 'Remember, it may be winter outside but it's summer under your arms!'

However, once they had recovered, they decided to give the programme a trial and use it as a convenient show to fit into the schedules wherever it suited, on Wednesday nights one week, Mondays another, sometimes running forty minutes, sometimes forty-five.

The first ever panel was composed of novelist Marghanita Laski, Canadian actress Barbara Kelly, comedian Jerry Desmonde and comedy scriptwriter Ted Cavanagh, and the first ever challenger was a barrow boy who sold fruit in a street off the Strand. Two minor alterations the BBC made to the American version were the introduction of the challengers' mime and a certificate for those who beat the panel. Eamonn always claimed that these were his ideas but they were, in fact, introduced by Leslie Jackson.

Originally the BBC intended Eamonn to take charge only every second week and gave him a rival who was to alternate with him with a view to deciding which should become permanent chairman – Gilbert Harding, who had been a very successful chairman on the radio quiz show 'Twenty Questions'.

Eamonn was fearful that Harding's intellectual ability, which he found intimidating, would quickly bring his new television career to an end. However, it was Harding's other, more famous facet, and one of which Eamonn was even more frightened, his renowned irascibility, that was the deciding factor. And it was not about to sink Eamonn's television career but to launch it.

Harding was in charge of the second edition of 'What's My

Line?' Besides being intellectual and irascible he was also renowned as a heavy drinker, and because of that it has become part of television folklore that his drinking caused him to get himself into the muddle which led to the rumpus that ended his brief reign as chairman. The pre-programme drinks he had that night very probably contributed to the intensity of the situation. But the real culprit was a callboy.

Somehow he got two challengers mixed up and sent on a motor mechanic when, in fact, the next challenger – and the one on Harding's programme running order – was supposed to be a male nurse.

'Has your job got anything to do with transport?' a panellist asked.

'Yes,' said the motor mechanic.

But Harding's mind was fixed on male nurse.

'No, it hasn't,' he almost yelled at the startled challenger.

'Do you use spanners in your work?' asked another panellist.

'Yes,' said the challenger.

'Oh, don't be so ridiculous!' roared Harding, thumping the desk. Then, to rid himself of what he thought was a practical joker, he announced, 'He's beaten the panel and he's a male nurse.'

'No I'm not,' bemoaned the bewildered man. 'I'm a motor mechanic.'

'Oh, are you?' retorted Harding. 'If that's the case I don't know what the devil's happening, but this is probably the last time I shall appear on television!'

With that declaration he left Eamonn unchallenged for the job of chairman, but it was not, of course, the last time he was to appear on television. He was persuaded to return as member of the show's panel a month later and his famed 'baiting' of Eamonn became one of the principal contributing factors to the success of the show and, because of the public sympathy it brought him, of Eamonn himself.

In the weeks that followed, Eamonn made a fairly smooth transition from radio to television. 'Perhaps it was because my introduction to it was through a panel game which required very little movement,' he said at the time.

But he was soon to find that there was one essential difference, even where a minimum of movement was called for. On television he had to wear a radio-microphone and he had a lot to learn about that.

His education started during a break in a rehearsal of the 'Line' when he excused himself from the studio and forgot what he had been told about switching off the mike.

When he returned he was puzzled as to why everybody had gone strangely quiet and then realised the eyes of the technicians and contestants were all on him. At first he thought he must have forgotten to do up his flies. But then the programme director told him the real reason. He began by switching off the microphone, then reminded him that while it was switched on every sound he made was broadcast loud and clear over the studio speakers, even when he was outside.

Such small local difficulties attended to, 'What's My Line?' was allowed to settle into a regular Sunday night slot and became as phenomenally successful in Britain as in America.

On one show in the first series, boxing promoter Jack Solomons, who was to have been the 'mystery guest', was unable to reach the studio because London was in the grip of one of the dense – and choking – smogs which blighted the capital throughout the Fifties. So Leslie Jackson suggested that Eamonn should be the 'mystery guest' as well as questionmaster.

So, when the panel donned their masks, Eamonn answered their questions in a falsetto voice while he announced the score in his own. He beat the panel.

At the start of its second series newspapers were saying the programme had 'outlived its welcome'; at the start of the third series the Daily Mail critic wrote, ' "What's My Line?" is now a lame duck'; and before taking it into its fourth series even its new producer, Dicky Leeman, wrote, 'It does not need clairvoyance to foresee the likelihood of this being the last series.'

The BBC hierarchy agreed with Leeman and announced that the final edition would be on March 20, 1955. Eamonn wrote a farewell message to the programme in his column in *The Star*. Then, at the end of that night's show, he cut a cake a viewer had specially baked; the last challenger, a specially chosen post-horn player, sounded a 'farewell'; and the panellists and production team held a 'wake' in the BBC club.

'What's My Line?' was replaced by another 'quiz' called 'Why?'.

The idea was that an adult challenger pretended to be a child while members of the panel played parents. Then after every statement a 'parent' made the 'child' asked 'Why?' until the panellist had to admit he or she could not think of a sensible answer with which to reply.

However, the moment it went on the air, viewers in their hundreds also started to ask 'Why?'

Why had the BBC been so idiotic as to put it on in the first place?

Why had the producers not had the common sense to realise that a child-imitator repeatedly asking the question 'why?' after practically every sentence would be as irritating as when a real child did the same thing (as many honest parents viewing immediately jammed the switchboard to point out)?

So the BBC said goodbye to 'Why?' almost immediately and made an appeal to the public for a panel-game to replace 'What's My Line?'. Naturally they were inundated with hundreds of bizarre and some not very seemly suggestions but the most common idea was for a programme called ... 'What's My Sideline?'

From this the BBC began to grasp that the viewers did not share their own view that 'What's My Line?' should be killed off and they brought it back for another series. And kept bringing it back for another seven years.

The programme was even to survive a scandal when, in November 1959, a national newspaper headline screamed '"What's My Line?" Rigged!' when, after leaving the panel, Marghanita Laski, said she had been given the name of a mystery guest, the novellist Ruby M. Ayers, in advance, and had then made a pretence of guessing her identity.

However, the backroom staff engaged to revive the programme years later for Thames TV who studied kinescopes smuggled out of the BBC – to remind them what the programme had looked like in those days – were convinced that was far from an isolated case.

Like the programme itself, some panellists were there by arrangement with Maurice Winnick. And it was believed by colleagues of hers that also by arrangement with Maurice Winnick one of the most famous of them, Lady Isobel Barnett, was given all the answers.

The production people looking at those old kinescopes paid special attention to the lady when they watched those kinescopes. In one show, Eamonn was about to flip over the final 'No' card as, without the tiniest clue to the challenger's occupation having emerged, the whole panel was apparently totally baffled. Then Lady Barnett suddenly called to the challenger, with absolute conviction: 'You're a popcorn popper! You pop popcorn!'.

She was right, of course. The contestant was indeed a lady who roasted maize until it was about to pop. So from nowhere Lady Barnett had got the correct answer. She had also achieved a second miracle. She had hit on the exact words that had been written on the programme caption to describe the job – 'Popcorn popper'.

Such shafts of intuition were explained away as 'inspired guesses'.

There are, of course, such phenomena as inspired guesses. I know because while I worked on the programme at Thames some panellists used to pester me to whisper them in their ears before the show and to avoid unpleasantness I, in my unctuous fashion, often did.

Despite the disaster of 'Why?' the BBC stubbornly kept trying to find another successor to 'What's My Line?' right throughout the Fifties. With varying degrees of success, most of it very little, they tried out such shows as 'Find The Link' 'The Name's The Same', 'Music, Music, Music', 'One of the Family', 'Ask Your Dad', 'What Do You Know?', 'Where on Earth?' 'Know Your Partner', 'Guess My Story' and 'Guess My Secret'.

'Guess My Secret' was one that did survive and, under its original title of 'I've Got A Secret', returned to the BBC in the Eighties with comedian Tom O'Connor in the chair. It was, originally, however, a cynical 'rip-off' of 'What's My Line?'

Not by someone who stole the idea from its owners and sold it at a handsome price to a competitior – but by someone who stole the idea from the owners and *sold it back to them.*

His name was Allan Sherman, and later in life he was to become famous as the singer-composer of folksong parodies such as 'Hello Mudda . . . Hello Fadda.'

At the time he said 'hello' to Mark Goodson and Bill Todman, whose American company owned 'What's My Line?', he was a young comedy writer in New York.

He approached them one day with a show to be called 'I've Got A Secret'. When he outlined the format for them they told him very pointedly that, but for a few minor variations, it was a copy of 'What's My Line?' and they certainly had no intention of buying something that had been stolen from them in the first place.

To their surprise, Sherman agreed with them. However, he went on calmly to suggest that they really should buy the 'rip-off' from him, because, he pointed out, if *they* didn't start copying their own shows, someone else would, and that someone would sell them to their competitors.

The logic and implicit threat behind Sherman's argument stopped Goodson and Todman from having him tossed out into the Manhattan street.

Instead they decided to bottle up their anger and buy 'I've Got A Secret' from him to be produced by their own company. Not only did they agree to pay a royalty for the format to Sherman – who was to die when he was at the height of his singing fame – they also put him on their pay roll as the programme's associate producer.

One other panel-game with which the BBC tried to replace 'What's My Line?' had the impossible title of 'Who's Whose?' This pearl of sophistication had an anonymous man seated in front of three anonymous women, or the same configuration with the sexes reversed, while a panel tried to deduce both by intuition and questions to which of the three the solo individual was married.

Apart from the fact that the panellists were seldom ever able to reach the correct conclusion it had one other drawback. It was one the BBC only spotted off-screen and it threatened to turn it in to a very avant-garde, adulterous version of 'Blind Date' which was not to arrive on our screens for another thirty years.

For after a few drinks in the hospitality room following one programme the male challenger appeared to ask one of the three married ladies, but not one to whom he was married, not 'Who's Whose?' but 'When? When?' Then they disappeared, and were later discovered in a nearby office doing what some 'Blind Date' contestants are only rumoured to get up to after they have been paired off and are unblinkered.

After that Auntie Beeb decided the programme was altogether too risky and killed it off. They resisted the suggestion claimed to have been made by Frank Muir and Denis Norden, who were BBC comedy writers at the time, that they keep it going but with the new title 'Who *Was* Whose?'

The search for a successor to 'What's My Line?' prompted Eamonn, himself, to try his skill at inventing a quiz-show. The result was the very modest 'Penny Posers', a general knowledge quiz in which the contestants started off with three pence and gained or lost one penny for each correct or incorrect answer. The whole quiz ran only twelve minutes and was broadcast for just six weeks on radio as a segment of 'The Forces Show'.

Years later he devised a somewhat more ambitious quiz called 'Whose Baby?' in which a panel had to guess which celebrity is a parent of a child introduced by the compère. It was a much more successful show and is still running on Thames Television more than a decade later.

The success of 'What's My Line?' must have been very much due to Eamonn, too, and not just its format, because, after he had parted company with them and joined Thames, the BBC tried to revive it with David Jacobs in the chair. But the audience reaction was poor and it lasted only one short series. Yet when, in 1984, Thames brought it back with Eamonn it was again a huge success – perhaps because some panellists' performances were enlivened in a way not strictly within the rules – and was still in production when he died three years later.

For Eamonn that early triumph with 'What's My Line?' emboldened him – he was then twenty-nine – to return briefly to Dublin to make a proposal of marriage to a twenty-three-year-old dancer he had met when he started presenting the quiz show at the Theatre Royal and where, for three years, she was a member of the resident chorus line.

Her name was Grace Bourke but later, on the day they married, he was to persuade her that like himself she should use the Gaelic version of her first name and change it to Grainne (pronounced Groynia). He felt that Grainne and Eamonn had a somewhat more resounding ring than plain old Grace and Eddie.

Grainne, jet black of hair and then a look-alike of Elizabeth Taylor, for whom she was later occasionally mistaken in expensive London restaurants, and once in the Lido nightclub in Paris, was just twenty-one when they first met – and said later she thought Eamonn seemed 'bumptious'.

She was one of seven children, four girls and three boys, of a family that was considerably wealthier than Eamonn's. Her father was Lorcan Bourke, one of Ireland's best known show business personalities, who ran a firm of theatrical costumiers and owned the Four Provinces Ballroom. He was also an impresario, producing shows that were stage-managed by his wife, Grainne's mother, Kathleen. Grainne was also related to two Irish playwrights. One of them was an uncle, her father's brother, Seamus de Burca. The other was a cousin and soon to become a more famous, or infamous, playwright. His name was Brendan Behan.

Grainne once played the part of a flirtatious French maid in a farce at Dublin's Peacock Theatre, 'Find The Island', written by her uncle. In one scene she wore a swimsuit, which was considered to be rather daring in the Dublin of the Forties.

Eamonn felt much more at ease with Grainne than with other girls because he first met her on a casual rather than formal basis in the easy-going atmosphere of Dublin show business and they had that and the Theatre Royal in common.

One night he met her when she was with her father, whom Eamonn also knew, in the bar of Dublin's Olympia Theatre. Her father was staging a revue at the theatre and Eamonn had called for a drink with friends. He had just bought his second car, a green Ford Prefect of which he was immensely proud, and which he wanted to show off. So, as they chatted, he asked Grainne if he could drive her home in it. She accepted.

On the journey, however, the engine suddenly stalled and when he said he had run out of petrol she wondered for a minute if, despite his gaucheness, Eamonn was trying on a line that had been invented with the motor-car itself.

But the car was, in fact, out of petrol. And what's more, although they could see the lights of a petrol station not far away, the would-be Lothario at the wheel was also out of money to buy more. As desperately he wriggled in his seat searching his pockets, the darkness hiding his blushes, Grainne took a 10/- note from her handbag and handed it to him. 'Here,' she said, 'buy some with this.'

Despite this clumsy start to their relationship, Grainne agreed to meet him again and soon they were seeing each other regularly, until Eamonn went to England with the Joe Loss Band show.

They wrote to each other frequently and Grainne followed his career as he got his first break on BBC radio and, the following year, on television.

That summer she toured the Continent with an aunt as chaperone and on the return journey they visited London – and Eamonn – for three days. The following weekend Eamonn took the boat to Dublin, drove Grainne down to the seafront at Dollymount and formally proposed by asking her the simple, unembellished question, 'Will you marry me?'.

Grainne accepted and Eamonn drove her home again. 'On the way,' she wrote later, 'he told me that he had badly wanted to ask me during my few days in London, but wouldn't do so because he hadn't told his mother.'

There was still Grainne's father to be faced, though. He did not get home until nearly three o'clock in the morning, after having had a few drinks with the boys, and was in a difficult mood. He and Eamonn went into the dining room while Grainne and her mother tried to listen through the closed door.

Late marriages were commonplace in Ireland and, at twenty-three, Lorcan did not think his daughter was yet ready for it. But, eventually, he gave his consent.

Eamonn and Grainne were married on November 7, 1951, at Corpus Christi Church, Dublin, Grainne wearing a gown of white lace she had designed herself and which, with the bridesmaid's dresses, was made at her father's costumiers.

Lorcan Burke, the impresario, took control of the wedding and made a huge production of it. There were seven bridesmaids, each in a gown made of twenty yards of white taffeta, and six groomsmen; invitations were sent to four hundred relatives and friends and the church was so packed the front doors had to be locked to prevent any more well-wishers from trying to squeeze in.

The first discovery Eamonn made as a married man was that he had run out of cigarettes.

So, on the way to the reception, with his bride of just half-an-hour beside him, he asked the driver of the wedding car to pull up at a pub so that he could get out and buy some.

The driver did better. He went into the pub to buy the cigarettes himself, knocked back a quick Irish whiskey and brought out two large ones for Eamonn and Grainne. Grainne took a sip of hers while Eamonn downed his in one. Then he lit a cigarette and they were on their way again, to the Four Provinces Ballroom where three bands played for the guests.

That evening Eamonn and Grainne drove to Limerick and then to Parknasilla a resort in Kerry, after which they later named their first marital house, for the honeymoon.

It seems it was not a very idyllic one, for Grainne later wrote, 'I don't think very much of honeymoons. I know I wouldn't want to go through mine again.'

Soon she would have many anxious moments to go through at the start of their marriage. And Eamonn, too, of course.

5

Grainne fights back
to fitness
and 'Life' begins

One relative who was not invited to Eamonn and Grainne's wedding was Brendan Behan. He would not have been able to accept it anyway because, at that time, the rebel Irish playwright was in an English jail.

He had first been arrested at the age of sixteen for his part in an IRA attempt to blow up a Merseyside shipyard and sent to Borstal, which gave rise to his play 'Borstal Boy'. Two years later he had been convicted in Dublin of the attempted murder of two Irish Special Branch detectives and sentenced to fourteen years' imprisonment but released by a general amnesty three years later. The following year he was again arrested in England, imprisoned in Manchester and deported back to Ireland twelve months after Eamonn and Grainne's wedding.

Eamonn did meet, and interview, Behan some years later however. It was a bold undertaking considering that not long before Behan, although himself not religiously inclined, had delivered the profound philosophical statement live on the Jack Parr Show on American television, 'The Protestant Religion was born in the bollocks of Henry VIII!'.

Eamonn had no need to risk a live interview, however. It was to be one of a series of interviews of famous Irishmen he intended to film and sell to America through one of his companies, the Eamonn Andrews Studios. His main problem was to interview Behan while he was sober.

The day before the interview he flew to Dublin and met Grainne's father and together they drove through a wet night to the tiny house of Behan's parents on a Dublin Council estate at Ballsbridge. From there they were to take Behan, and his wife, Beatrice, to a hotel in the seaside town of Bray, close to the Ardmore Film Studios, so they could make an early start the following morning before he could take on board too much liquor.

When they knocked, Behan himself came to the door, a giant of a man with a mop of black hair falling around his face, his shirt-front unbuttoned down to his navel, his sleeves rolled up to the elbows.

But as soon as he opened the door he slammed it shut in their faces again. Eamonn looked at his father-in-law through the falling rain. 'He's your relative, not mine,' he said. 'What are you going to do now?'

Bourke suggested they should return to the shelter of the car but then the door was opened again and Behan reappeared.

'Well, why don't you fuckin' come in?' he shouted.

'You shut the door,' said Eamonn.

'Oh, I was only trying to keep the fuckin' cat in,' said Behan.

In the house's little living room were two other men. One, an unshaven character standing by the fireplace, Behan introduced as an artist. The other, who was sitting glassy-eyed on a settee wearing a threadbare overcoat and a greasy cap, an open bottle of stout in his hand, he did not introduce at all. He explained that his wife was upstairs packing a bag.

Behan did not have a very high regard for Eamonn. He considered him to be a somewhat prissy representative of the Irish nation, and this led to some less than poetic exchages between them that evening.

First, however, he brought out a bottle of Irish whiskey and poured some into two glasses which he handed to Eamonn and Bourke.

Then he said to Eamonn, 'You know, you think *you're* fuckin' famous, but I've got *my* fuckin' fans, too, you know. I came here from Dublin airport today and, do you know, the fuckin' taxi driver wouldn't let me pay the fuckin' fare. He recognized me and wouldn't take a fucking' penny.'

Behan went on for some time about the taxi driver and the

pleasure of getting such recognition and the driver rewarding his talent by giving him a free ride.

Then his wife came in with the packed bag and all of them, except the figure on the settee who had not uttered a single word, started to leave. As they filed out Beham picked up the nearly full whiskey bottle and pushed it into one of the man's overcoat pockets. 'There you are,' he said, 'that's for you,' and stepped through the door.

As Eamonn followed him he turned to the artist and, indicating the still figure on the settee, asked quietly, 'Who is that fella?'

To which the artist replied, 'Oh him? He's the fuckin' taxi driver.'

After that, however, their plan of operations went surprisingly smoothly and Eamonn got his interview without too much trouble. But the idea to produce a series of such interviews faltered at the next hurdle. The subject they chose was another Irish playwright, Sean O'Casey. O'Casey, however, would not go along with the idea. He wrote back to say the only way he would be seen on film with Eamonn would be if the normal situation was reversed and he did the interviewing.

As Brendan Behan's international reputation – and notoriety – increased with the filming of his play 'The Quare Fellow', so did the number of both Eamonn's colleagues and members of the viewing public who were suggesting that he should feature him on 'This Is Your Life', which was then still being produced by the BBC.

Understandably, even the prospect of confronting Behan for a taped programme made Eamonn very nervous. But he felt he had to answer mounting insinuations from people, many of them his fellow countrymen who had not seen his filmed interview, nor ever would, that he was frightened of Behan; was, in fact, too timid to give him the accolade so many thought he deserved.

To try to quieten those critics Eamonn came up with a bizarre compromise.

He decided to do Behan's father's 'Life' instead. This meant he would be seen to be coming face to face with Behan, albeit as a contributor to his father's story rather than as the 'subject'. It still did not make a lot of sense to the viewers, however, because although he was a puckish, talkative character, Behan Senior made his living in the unextraordinary job of housepainter.

And it made even less sense when it was transmitted because both the old man and many of the other people who appeared on the programme spoke with such rich Dublin accents – the kind that had been 'elocuted' out of Eamonn – that few of the British viewers could understand a word they said.

First, however, there had – again – been the problem of getting Brendan Behan in front of the cameras.

Because of his reputation the producer decided that only Eamonn, rather than a stranger of a researcher, was likely to be able to persuade him to appear on the programme.

Eamonn eventually agreed, but very reluctantly because he had always refused to involve himself in the work of programme organising. He was sorry immediately.

At the time, Behan was somewhere in France where he had gone 'to dry out' – a somewhat unusual destination for someone engaged in such an undertaking – and it took Eamonn days to locate him by telephone.

When he finally got him on the end of the line Behan immediately asked, 'How much is the fuckin' fee?'

Eamonn reminded him that Stephen was his father, after all. And he explained that it was not the policy of the programme to pay people to say nice things about the subjects of 'This Is Your Life' (there were later to be many exceptions to this rule) in case they, or the programme, were later accused of insincerity. He did not mention this was also a very opportune way of persuading some of the most famous international names in showbusiness to appear without being paid the huge fees they would otherwise command.

By the time Eamonn finally convinced him he would not be getting a fee for paying a verbal tribute to his father, he knew Behan had not dried out all that much because, although by then ten years had passed, Behan started to lambast him for not inviting his mother, Kathleen, who was of course, related to Grainne, to his wedding. (Kathleen was herself a great Dublin character who, in her will, bequeathed £100 each to half a dozen of her friends to go out and enjoy themselves – but unfortunately only left a total of £4.50.)

Eventually, however, Eamonn persuaded him to take part in the programme which, because it was so much orientated in that city, was being made as an outside broadcast in Dublin.

His troubles had only just started, however.

When he walked onto the programme Behan totally ignored him and barely even acknowledged his father. Instead he started to peer into the audience where he spotted the former Irish rugby union player, Tony O'Reilly, who was later to become chairman of the huge American company Heinz International – in Ireland they call him the Bean Baron – and spent nearly three minutes telling the rest of them all about him.

When Eamonn finally persuaded him to sit down, Behan took out a packet of French cigarettes and offered him one. When Eamonn declined he looked offended and said, 'Oh, of course, with all this television you can afford more expensive ones, can't you.'

The sight of the cigarettes made Behan's father feel like a smoke, too. He pulled out an old pipe and started to search his pockets for his tobacco.

Eamonn realised that he must have left it in the pocket of his overcoat which was backstage and, while Behan started a conversation with his father, he managed to whisper a message to the floor manager.

One of the production team retrieved a brown paper bag from the overcoat and gave it to another of Behan's relatives who slipped it to the grateful Behan Senior when he went on to greet him.

The old man filled his pipe with the mixture and started to light it. Eamonn, who was desperately trying to keep some control over the mayhem as members of the Behan family completely disregarded him and instead chatted to each other, almost lost his concentration completely as he watched the odd behaviour of the father of the family, for he was screwing up his nose and contorting his face as he struck match after match in a vain effort to light the pipe.

It was only when the programme had come to its untidy conclusion that it was realised that old man Behan had put two brown paper bags in his overcoat pockets. One contained tobacco. The contents of the other, which he had desperately been trying to light in his pipe, was for use during breaks in his housepainting. It was a mixture of tea and sugar.

In Dublin the 'Life' of 'The Quare Fellow's' father was, naturally considered a stunning success. But in London members of the BBC hierarchy were shaking their heads and mumbling that the decision to risk taking the programme there, and the incomprehensible result, was a sign it was running out of steam.

But those worries were still way in the future when Eamonn and Grainne first set up home in England in a first floor flat in West Hampstead, London.

They were separated for long periods almost immediately, however, because Eamonn was now presenting the radio programme 'Welcome To Britain' which meant he spent most of his time touring the country, returning to London only at weekends for 'What's My Line?'

Eamonn hated those separations and when he looked back on that period of his life ten years later he wrote in his autobiography, 'I am sure that one of the main reasons for the high mortality rate among show business marriages is the continual separation of husband and wife.'

It was a sentiment which now could be interpreted as sadly prophetic in a way he did not intend, because when he died of heart disease in 1987, at the age of sixty-four, he had been subjecting himself to such separations from Grainne – who had declared her preference for a family home in Ireland rather than England in 1970 – for seventeen years.

During that time he presented 'This Is Your Life' for thirty-nine weeks every single year, fronted the nightly magazine show 'Today' for ten years as well as periods with 'Time For Business', 'Top Of The World', and revivals of 'The Eamonn Andrews Show' and 'What's My Line?' It meant that for all those years, which included occasional trips to America, the Continent and to other parts of the British Isles, he split his time between England and Ireland, flying to London and then back again to Dublin, in all nearly one thousand times.

Grainne badly missed life in Dublin from the very start. After they had lived in London for only six months she wrote to her aunt Maureen, her father's sister, 'I'm unhappy sometimes. I would come back to Ireland if I didn't love Eamonn so much.'

Five months after they were married Eamonn invited his mother to visit them in West Hampstead and arranged a dinner party to welcome her to which he also invited Gilbert Harding and the other 'What's My Line?' panellists.

Before they arrived, Grainne started to prepare the meal in one of the new pressure cookers that had just gone on the market and which Harding had given them as a wedding present. But as she stood working at the stove, the cooker suddenly exploded and shot boiling liquid into her face.

In pain and terror she ran to the sink, turned the cold tap full on and held her face under the water. Thanks to that quick thinking, and although she needed medical treatment for three weeks, her face was hardly marked.

A year later Grainne was in severe pain again, but this time there was no apparent reason.

She felt it in her knee but when it failed to respond to treatment, and she had been limping badly for a month, an X-ray revealed that it was referred pain from a tubercular infection of the hip.

She went into Stanmore Orthopaedic Hospital, Middlesex, where Eamonn visited her once, sometimes twice, a day.

He was also left with the responsibility of looking after their pet poodle, which not surprisingly considering the continuing success of 'What's My Line?' they had named 'Quiz'. Driving home to their flat in West Hampstead late one stormy night after dining with friends in Bloomsbury, Eamonn lost his way near Euston station and got out of the car to ask directions of a policeman who was sheltering in a shop doorway. When he got home he discovered the dog was missing.

To his added distress it happened just after Grainne had asked him to bring the poodle with him on one of his next visits to the hospital.

He immediately returned to the Euston area and started driving slowly around, close to the kerb, his eyes desperately scouring the empty streets between there and King's Cross station, which he did not realise was a notorious 'red light' district.

After half an hour he noticed a police patrol was following him and now it overtook and signalled him to stop. The two policemen who got out could not believe their eyes. Here was the one and only famous, God-fearing, church-going television star Eamonn Andrews caught kerb-crawling! Well, well, you never can tell.

Eamonn was naturally appalled at the reason they suggested he was in such a place in the early hours of the morning.

Then, why else was he driving so slowly through those infamous streets? Eamonn, protested that he was looking for a dog, not a prostitute. Presumably then, he had done the obvious thing and first reported the loss of the dog to the police? Er, no, he had not thought of that.

So it went on until he was finally able to convince them he really was searching for the missing poodle and they let him continue. He carried on searching until he was almost out of petrol.

The next day the police phoned him to say that someone had momentarily caught the dog but it had slipped its collar and run off again. However, two days later, a couple reported finding a somewhat dishevelled poodle near their home in Grays Inn Road from where Eamonn recovered it, happily unharmed.

Grainne was in hospital for nine months. Her weight ballooned by four stones – she was not allowed to diet – and, because of the pain caused by her hip, she was only able to walk with the aid of crutches.

But then she started to make a slow recovery and when she was finally ready to leave the hospital Eamonn made it a memorable homecoming. He collected her in a brand-new Ford Zephyr convertible and took her to a new home he had prepared for them, a spacious, four-bedroomed ground floor flat in London's Lancaster Gate. Then he drove her to the South of France for a five week holiday, while an Australian actor, Ron Randell, took over as chairman of 'What's My Line?'.

When they returned to London she took a course of physiotherapy and was eventually able to walk with only the aid of one stick and, three years after the illness had first struck, she could, at least, walk normally again. She was now allowed to go on a diet but it took her another year to lose the extra four stones in weight.

It was generally believed that the fact they never had children of their own was due to Grainne's hip condition and whenever that was said, or written, Eamonn never contradicted it. But shortly after he died, Grainne said, for the first time, that was not the reason. However, she did not say anything more.

As Grainne returned to full health, Eamonn's success continued apace. On television he added two children's programmes 'Crackerjack' and 'Playbox' to 'What's My Line?', while on radio he was presenting 'Sports Report' throughout the whole of Saturday afternoon and a late night interview show, 'Pied Piper'. He was now also making frequent boxing commentaries – which many believed to the time of his death was his one broadcasting skill – and the following year he broadcast his first world heavyweight title fight from San Francisco, between British champion Don Cockell and Rocky Marciano of America.

Before leaving for San Francisco for the fight he let it be known to the producers of the American 'What's My Line?' that he would be stopping over in New York and, as a result, was invited to make a guest appearance as a panellist on the show there.

He was very nervous and excited about the prospect of making his debut on American television, and on the most watched show in the country at that. He also felt that, as with panellists of the British version, it would be purely a matter of turning up half-an-hour beforehand, appearing on the show, then retiring to the hospitality room for convivial drinks.

He found he was mistaken. The show's creators Mark Goodson and Bill Todman were determined their visitor from England would not do or say anything on the programme that would make him sound foolish to American ears. So they spent the whole of one morning meticulously schooling Eamonn on how the show was run there, the differences in programme terminology (such as 'moderator' instead of chairman) and between many American and English expressions, the distinctions between Government, Federal and State laws, even the kind of questions he should ask.

On the night, all went well until actor Peter Lawford came on as the mystery guest and in the decade of discs, cassettes, LPs, EPs and albums, Eamonn asked him, 'Mister Mystery Guest, do you make gramophone records?'

While Eamonn sat mystified, the audience hooted and the other panellists laughed so hard they nearly unmasked themselves.

During that trip to America, Eamonn saw a new show called 'This Is Your Life', but was uncertain if it was the kind of programme British audiences would take to.

However, when he returned to London, Ronnie Waldman, the BBC's then Head of Light Entertainment, told him he had not only seen the programme himself but was already trying to persuade his bosses to give it a trial. He asked Eamonn if he would be prepared to present it. Eamonn agreed, although not with the greatest of confidence that Waldman would get the Corporation's blessing or that, if he did, the programme would be a success.

Nevertheless, Waldman eventually broke down the BBC's resistance to the programme, although they were still so fearful it would be too intrusive and sickly sentimental that they decided it would be produced only on a monthly basis. Then, should they want to be shot of it again, they could quietly drop it without too much fuss. In fact, the programme went out only once a month for the first six months and then became a fortnightly show for a further two years before the BBC had the confidence to turn it into a weekly production.

After it became the success it did, Eamonn liked it to be believed that he was responsible for it becoming a BBC production as, later, he also gave the impression it was entirely through him that Thames revived it in 1969. Perhaps over the years he genuinely convinced himself that had been the case.

To get the first 'This Is Your Life' safely launched, the BBC brought over the American compère and deviser of the programme, Ralph Edwards, to present it, and his back-up team to produce it.

Many people believe Edwards simply sat down one day and dreamed up 'This Is Your Life'. In fact, it was originally a radio show. Or, more precisely, a part of a radio show called 'Truth or Consequences' which Edwards, a one-time radio scriptwriter, announcer and newsreader, also devised and presented.

During the war he had been considered something of a hero on the home front when, through his radio show, he won 'The Eisenhower Award' for the number of war bonds he persuaded Americans to buy.

A year after the war, psychiatrists at a Los Angeles hospital asked for his help. They explained that many of the servicemen who had lost limbs or been paralysed by wounds were afraid to return home because they thought they would not be accepted back into the community.

The doctors asked him if, through his programme, he would help try to convince them this would not be the case.

Edwards agreed. As an experiment, he invited a war-wounded paraplegic named Lawrence Tranter to the studio and, to convince him they still cared for him, he secretly brought together all of his family, together with his friends from pre-army days. These he 'sprang' on the wounded soldier one by one to punctuate a potted biography of his life. Then, when they were all gathered around him, he said, 'Lawrence Tranter, this is your life past and present. But what of the future?'

Tranter told him he wanted to be a jeweller. Edwards, who had been apprised of this likelihood in advance, promised him a year's training with a school of watchmakers and financial help in setting him up in business – in his home town. The emotional effect of it all on the listeners was little short of fantastic.

As the number of 'Truth or Consequences' programmes given over to the 'rehabilitation' exercise increased, Edwards decided to turn it into a separate show, first on radio then, in 1951, and now intended for entertainment more than therapy, on television. By then he had cut the summing up sentence to 'This Is Your Life' and that became its title and its very famous catch-phrase.

An attractive but not very numerate lady announcer on Tyne Tees Television endorsed this in her own way when she once breathlessly introduced the programme, 'And now, the three most famous words in television, "This Is Your Life"!'

The programme was such a big success on American television that the networks wanted an edition of it every week, all year round. It was not until six years later, in 1957, that Edwards was able to take a brief break from it. To present it in his absence he chose a Hollywood actor named Ronald Reagan.

What to call the person the programme was about was always a problem. 'Lifer', the term sometimes used, had somewhat grim connotations. 'Victim', the favourite of newspapers, Eamonn always insisted had suggestions of cruelty about it (to which cynics among those he was addressing would shrug and say 'So?').

Edwards preferred the somewhat grandiose 'Guest of honour'. While occasionally using that term too, particularly when the person in the chair was somebody to whom he was being craftily obsequious, Eamonn settled for 'the subject' and to the members of his team (including myself) that is what it forever became.

The first 'subject' of the British version of 'This Is Your Life' was intended to be English international footballer Stanley (later Sir Stanley) Matthews. But a national newspaper, the since defunct *Daily Sketch*, decided it was going to get itself a big exclusive by finding out the name the BBC was, quite understandably in the circumstance, determined to keep secret.

A team of reporters was instructed to draw up a list of the

principal celebrities of the day, mark those who would be likely candidates for the programme and systematically work their way through it, telephoning relatives of all of them with a phoney message congratulating them on the fact that a member of the family had been chosen as the new show's first 'honoured guest!'

With four days to go to transmission one got round to Matthews and rang his brother. 'I'll bet the family's delighted that Stanley's going to be the first guest of honour on "This Is Your Life",' said the reporter.

'We certainly are,' said the brother. 'But how did you know?'

'I didn't know for sure,' said the reporter. 'Until you just told me.'

The story broke on a Tuesday morning. The programme was due to be transmitted live the following Friday.

It was Edwards who saved the situation. By then used to similar setbacks on the show in America he realised the only way to create a replacement programme in that time was to choose a subject whose life would be relatively easy to research and whose friends and relatives would appreciate the need for urgency and co-operation. The most obvious candidate was Eamonn himself.

To prevent him becoming suspicious, they told him they were mounting a show on former world light-heavyweight boxing champion Freddie Mills. But on July 29, 1955, Eamonn himself became the first ever subject of the first ever British version of 'This Is Your Life'.

Twenty years later the producers at Thames made him the subject a second time. By then, thanks to Ralph Edward's work in getting it safely launched, 'This Is Your Life' had made Eamonn the most successful and probably the richest, British television performer ever.

But when Edwards paid another visit to England with his wife at about that time he was very hurt by Eamonn's apparent total lack of gratitude.

They went to see Eamonn present the show for Thames and to their surprise and bitter disappointment he totally ignored their presence there.

They had let him know in advance that they would be in the studio audience which, at that time, numbered only 120.

After the programme had finished and the cameras had been

switched off, Eamonn, as usual, thanked all the guests and the audience. Edwards then expected him to acknowledge him as the man who had devised the programme and who had made Eamonn himself the very first subject of it in Britain.

But Eamonn did not even mention him.

'He totally ignored us,' Edwards told me years later at his home in Beverly Hills. 'My wife was even more hurt for my sake than I was myself. What was worse, we had a woman friend with us and she was so livid about what she reckoned had been an outrageous snub that she wanted to go to Eamonn's dressing room afterwards and tell him so.'

What Edwards was unaware of was that there was nothing personal in this. It came naturally to Eamonn never publicly to acknowledge any of the many people who had helped him to reach the top of his profession. He preferred as many people as possible to be under the illusion that all his achievement was due to his own talent and hard labour. It was part of the formula of his success and – as even Edwards would have agreed – the important thing was that it worked.

6

Booted out by
Blanchflower –
and by the BBC

Almost immediately 'This is Your Life' was launched in 1955 it was accused by critics of being intrusive. During the 'Life' of Anna (later Dame Anna) Neagle, a clip of film was shown of her dancing with Jack Buchanan, her matinee idol partner in the romantic British film musicals produced by her husband, Herbert Wilcox, who had died not long before.

Immediately Buchanan's features flickered on the screen Dame Anna burst into uncontrollable sobbing. Apart from finding this an unacceptable occurrence on British television, outraged viewers took it as an involuntary confirmation of the suspicions that she had been in love with Buchanan off as well as on the screen for years.

The following day one national newspaper's headline demanded: 'This key-hole snooping must stop!'

Such demonstrations of indignation, real or imagined, of course only prompted more viewers to make a beeline for the peep-hole and served to assure the show's rating success. Another boost came when, because he said he agreed with the sentiment expressed in that headline, footballer Danny Blanchflower, the captain of Northern Ireland and Tottenham Hotspur, became the first person to say 'no' to Eamonn when he confronted him with the book.

Blanchflower, who also wrote newspaper articles and regularly contributed to radio and television sports programmes, was lured to a BBC studio by Eamonn's boss on 'Sports Report', Angus McKay, with an invitation to a phoney discussion programme about the then controversial issue of footballers' wages.

Blanchflower was told that Eamonn would also be taking part. But when he saw him suddenly whip the book from under a table, indicate that a camera was now switched on, and say, 'Tonight, Danny Blanchflower, This Is Your Life', the footballer said, 'Oh no it's not,' and dashed for the studio door.

As Eamonn's nervous smile was suddenly replaced by a look of amazed bewilderment McKay made a grab for Blanchflower and caught him by the coat. But Blanchflower wriggled out of it, charged through the door and ran down a flight of stone steps.

However, the door beyond the steps was locked and Eamonn was able to catch up with him, pleading with him to change his mind. 'Think of all the relatives and friends we've lined up for you ... think how disappointed they'll be if you don't go through with it.'

'That's your problem, you invited them,' said Blanchflower. 'Open this door.'

Eamonn asked him to think about the work that had gone into the programme ... the money it had cost ... the audience waiting in another studio. But Blanchflower was adamant. Finally, the door was unlocked. He took his coat from McKay and left.

Sometime afterwards Blanchflower told me, 'There was never the slightest chance Andrews's famous blarney would persuade me to change my mind and I thought his attempts to try to amounted to little less than blackmail.

'In fact, the programme itself is an instrument of blackmail. If a victim refuses it suggests there is something in his life he wants to hide.'

There was so much speculation as to why Blanchflower refused that he called a press conference to explain that his decision had nothing to do with him being afraid of his life being laid bare and everything to do with the fact that he disliked the very nature of the programme.

'What's more,' Blanchflower added, in our conversation, 'as it turned out I hated at least a third of the people who were supposed to come on and say nice things about me. It would have been hypocritical if I had pretended I was glad to see them or given the impression I believed they meant what they were saying.'

Blanchflower's snub of Eamonn of course also improved the

programme's appeal. It convinced viewers there really was the danger of the subject leaving Eamonn with egg on his face just when they were becoming sceptical of it ever happening. From then on the question in the viewers' minds when Eamonn prepared to spring on a subject – and indeed in the minds of the production team when they selected one – was, 'Will he do a Blanchflower?'

Richard Gordon the author of the 'Doctor' books was the second to 'do a Blanchflower.' He said no or, more precisely, 'Oh balls!' when Eamonn confronted him not long after Thames Television had started producing the programme.

But Gordon could not run as fast as Blanchflower. Eamonn caught him as he tried to open a studio door which also happened to be locked but this time those same exhortations, which by then Eamonn had fashioned into a plea that would soften the hardest of hearts, or most embarrassed of souls, persuaded him to change his mind.

That widely headlined encounter nearly did not happen, however. The programme's original plan was for the confrontation to be pre-recorded at an outside location (in which case the company would have been obliged to cut the offending word). But because of a demarcation dispute it had to be scrapped at the last minute and in a desperate bid to save the show from being junked, too, the production team managed to lure Gordon into the studio almost on the dot of transmission time.

So, by a stroke of sheer good fortune – which had at first promised disaster for the programme – Gordon's anatomical answer to Eamonn's invitation was transmitted live and so, accidentally, gave its viewing figures one of their best boosts ever.

A third, but unpublicised turn down, came in 1985 when Eamonn confronted Harry Andrews in a street in London's West End. When the veteran actor realised what was happening he shouted out, 'Oh, you shit!', pushed Eamonn away and made a dash for it.

But he had only taken a couple of steps before Eamonn managed to stop him from running in the roadway – which was fortunate for both the actor and the programme because at that moment he was rushing into the path of an oncoming double-decker bus.

Again Eamonn came out with the well rehearsed think-of-the-disappointment-it-will-etcetera routine and the actor finally acquiesced. The programme went ahead, with the offending words deleted, but right throughout it the actor scarcely ever betrayed a smile and certainly never shed a tear.

Another bonus 'This Is Your Life' gained from these rare hostile receptions was that they appeared to confirm the sincerity of Eamonn's frequently stated claim that he would never go ahead with a programme if he had reason to believe the subject was in on the secret and would be shamming surprise.

From time to time, however, and despite the publicity given to that claim, Eamonn found reason to go back on it.

He felt it wise to do so with – of all people – Danny Blanchflower.

His reason was that it would be 'for the good of the programme' because if, at a later date, Blanchflower let him go ahead with it after all, it would counteract the adverse criticism 'This Is Your Life' got in the debate that followed his walk-out. (Maybe it did not occur to Eamonn that it would have been a great personal coup, too.)

Later Blanchflower said he was astonished when Eamonn approached him at a public function and asked him – 'now I'd had more time to think it over' – if he would go along with the programme if he was 'surprised' a second time.

'I told him I certainly would not and I was amazed that he even suggested it,' said Blanchflower. 'He just shrugged and walked off.'

Years later Eamonn tried the same ploy on comedy actor Derek Nimmo.

Nimmo was to have been one of the first subjects of 'This Is Your Life' when Thames began to produce it in 1969. But days before somebody – believed to be an actor who had first been asked to appear and then told he was not required – slipped a note under the dressing room door at a West End theatre telling him all about it.

So Nimmo phoned the programme's production office and told them he knew. Shortly afterwards Eamonn phoned him at the theatre. He was anxious that his brand new, lucrative series should get off to a smooth and, apparently trouble-free start.

'He told me that a tremendous amount of time and money had been spent on preparing the programme,' Nimmo said later, 'and what a setback it would be so soon into the new series if it was all wasted. Then he asked me if I would just go along with it and pretend to be surprised. I told him I could not possibly agree to such a thing.'

These two attempts at fooling the public may have failed but, as he battled to keep turning out the programme at Thames Television year upon year, Eamonn became adept at a whole range of deceits.

However, on at least one occasion during the show's year at the BBC it was, himself and the whole production team that were stunningly deceived.

It was a 'Life' that brought a lump to the throats of the nation; the story of wartime seamen, Tom Evans, taken prisoner by the Japanese after his ship, the cruiser HMS Exeter, was sunk in the Battle of the Java Sea, and forced to work in a labour gang in the Nagasaki dockyards with sixty-six other British prisoners.

The audience listened aghast as Eamonn told of Tom's experiences as the second atomic bomb fell on Nagasaki; how there was a blinding flash; a sky that turned from fierce blue to sickening brown; a roaring and shuddering like a massive earthquake; a mushroom cloud of smoke that blotted out the sun.

How could any man survive this? Tom did, the astonished audience learned from Eamonn, because he risked death at the hands of his guards by sneaking off behind a stone wall to smoke a cigarette, a stone wall which amazingly withstood the blast and miraculously shielded him from the deadly radiation.

Then tears were shed throughout the land as Eamonn told touchingly how later Tom learned that all of his sixty-five pals had perished in the holocaust and he had been the sole survivor. It was the very stuff of 'This Is Your Life'. Such a shame not a word of it was true.

Afterwards, journalists investigated Tom's astonishing story of survival more thoroughly than the programme's researchers had. They discovered Evans had been nowhere near Nagasaki when the bomb fell, and not one British prisoner of war had been killed by it in any case.

His story had been a complete fabrication. He had started to tell his wartime exploits to the regulars in the Windsor pub where he was landlord and they had got better by the pint. When one of them suggested his would make a good 'This Is Your Life' story, the programme team grabbed at it.

When Eamonn was told he had presented the 'accolade' to a complete phoney, and millions of viewers had been fooled, he shrugged it off. 'There *must* have been an element of truth somewhere in the story,' he insisted. 'Anyway, I don't want to know. It's done now and I never look back.'

It may have been a principle of his never to look back (if it was not a pretty sight) but there was plenty he had to look forward to when he returned to Ireland in 1960, exactly ten years after leaving there as a music hall quiz show host with occasional jobs on radio. For Eamonn was back in Dublin with the most powerful job in Irish broadcasting – chairman of the advisory committee set up by the Irish Government to establish a television service in the country.

He was not a unanimous choice. By then his Eamonn Andrews Studios were doing good business selling packaged programmes to Radio Eireann. An opposition spokesman in the Irish Parliament expressed 'profound regret and grave disquiet that his appointment disregarded the principle that there should be no conflict of interests in any public authority'. His appointment was also linked to the resignation of Radio Eireann's then Director of Broadcasting, Maurice Gorham, although Gorham himself did not confirm the connection.

There were reports at the time that he was chosen because he supported the governing Fianna Fail party although Eamonn was far too shrewd ever publicly to declare any political partisanship for parties either in Ireland or Britain.

Nor did he ever reveal his attitude to the warring factions in Ireland and the 'This Is Your Life' team only heard him even refer to them on one occasion. That was when a suggestion was made that the Catholic boxer and then world featherweight champion Barry McGuigan should be the subject of the programme and to enhance the atmosphere it should be an outside broadcast from the stadium in his native Belfast.

Eamonn refused. 'I'd stand no chance,' he said. 'I'd be shot by both sides.'

As it was, he came close to being accidentally shot when he surprised soldier and explorer Lieutenant-Colonel John Blashford-Snell for his 'Life'.

Blashford-Snell had served in Northern Ireland and because of this he had been given a bodyguard. However, so zealous had been the Ministry of Defence about abiding with the request to keep the programme secret from him, that they also neglected to tell his bodyguard or to tell the production team about the bodyguard.

To lure him to a location suitable for a confrontation 'Blashers' was told he was to be interviewed by BBC radio about a forthcoming exploring venture he was planning. Then, as he was walking across London's Portland Place towards Broadcasting House, Eamonn suddenly stepped out of the shadows and in front of him.

Understandably, this alerted the bodyguard who was even more alarmed to hear an Irish voice. And, acording to what another member of the party told Eamonn afterwards, his gun was in his hand and already cocked when he recognised him and realised what was happening.

At 'This Is Your Life' programme meetings, Eamonn sometimes revealed how conscious he was of potential dangers when his glance under his chair before he sat down was more obvious than usual.

When one of those present naively made a reference to the fact that he had looked under the chair before sitting on it, he replied, 'Doesn't everybody?'

In Dublin, Eamonn turned down the permanent job of first Director-General of the new Irish Radio and Television authority, deciding that he preferred to be in front of the cameras rather than in a seat of power behind them. Instead he stayed on in the honorary role of Authority chairman until Ireland's television service had successfully been established.

Two years later, he was paid the compliment of being asked to play the major role in another piece of television history making. This time it was at the invitation of the BBC who engaged him to front the first ever live transmission from Britain to America via the newly launched US communications satellite 'Telstar'.

To these accolades the British Government added an honorary CBE. But despite them and his success as presenter of the two most watched television programmes of the day, when a mutual friend attempted to introduce him to Lord Reith, the legendary first-ever Director General of the BBC completely snubbed him.

Eamonn was having dinner at Claridges one evening with a former BBC Governor and his wife when Reith walked in with a young lady companion. He spotted the ex-Governor and stopped to chat to him while the young lady talked to Eamonn about the previous week's 'This Is Your Life'.

Eamonn's dining companion then broke off his conversation with Reith and said to him. 'By the way, I don't know if you have met Eamonn Andrews . . .'

But Reith ignored what he had said and continued with the conversation. Presuming he had not quite heard the first time the ex-Governor made a second, more precisely enunciated attempt at the introduction. But, to the embarrassment of the rest of the party, Reith again went on talking.

Eamonn, understandably, was very hurt by the snub. Later he declared that he did not look on it as a personal rebuff by Reith but that it was an indication of the Scotsman's distaste for any programme he considered to be less than serious.

He also considered himself fortunate he was not at the time working for commercial television or there was no knowing what Reith would have said – or done – when their mutual acquaintance attempted to effect that introduction. For when Parliament passed the Independent Television Act in 1954 Reith described it as the 'arrival of the Black Plague'.

Eamonn and Grainne celebrated ten years of marriage by moving into a large house on the river Thames, close to Chiswick bridge, for which, in 1961, they paid £21,000. Money was no problem. By then he had become one of the highest paid, if not the highest paid, performers on British television.

He could also have been one of the highest paid in the world. The previous year, when he was in New York to commentate on the world heavyweight championship between America's Floyd Patterson and Ingemar Johansson of Sweden, he made his fifth appearance as a guest-panellist on the American 'What's My Line?'. Afterwards one of the show's owners, Mark Goodson, took him to dine at the 21 Club.

During the meal he offered Eamonn $250,000 dollars a year to replace John Daly, who had already been doing the job for a decade and was something of television legend, as chairman of the American show. That would have been only *part* of the money he could have earned.

For that he would have been expected to arrive at the studios only an hour before the show was transmitted and, half-an-hour later, the show over, he would be finished with it for a week. With just one other show he could, like Daly, have earned another quarter-of-a-million dollars a year, together with many thousands more for public and guest-appearances – or a total of the equivalent of at least seven times as much as he was being paid by the BBC.

He turned it down. The reason he gave me later was that as his father had died not long before he felt it would take him too far away from his mother, and that worried him even though his three sisters and his brother, Noel – by then well established as a Radio Eireann sports commentator – still lived close to her in Dublin.

Although he did not say as much, another reason was almost certainly Grainne. It was unlikely she would have settled for life in New York. She still talked of returning to Dublin.

By then she and Eamonn were also reconciled to the fact that they would not have any children of their own and had started to think about adoption. Eamonn was not sure how he felt about the idea himself but, once they had settled in the house in Chiswick, Grainne made the decision. On the evening of their eleventh wedding anniversary she announced to Eamonn that she wanted to adopt a child.

Shortly afterwards they contacted a Catholic adoption society and a few months later they brought home baby Emma for the start of the six months fostering period before her adoption could be made final. The joy of having a baby in the house was mixed with the irritation of having to accept regular visits by officials going through the routine of satisfying themselves they really would make satisfactory parents. In addition was the anxiety of knowing that, at any time during the period, the child's mother was entitled to demand the child back without giving any reason.

That anxiety nearly caused ex-boxer Eamonn to throw a punch for the first and only time since he had quit the ring.

They tried to keep the news of their intention to adopt secret from the media for those first six months in case the story was seen by the mother. The danger was that emotion caused by reading such a report could lead to a change of mind by any mother whose baby had been fostered with a view to adoption at about that time, including Emma's who, of course, did not know who the prospective parents were.

There was just one month to go when the worst happened and the news leaked out and the newspapers carried stories that famous television celebrity Eamonn Andrews was adopting a baby. Naturally they all wanted photographs, too.

Eamonn anxiously explained to their editors that he and Grainne were already fearful the stories themselves might cause them to lose Emma but a photograph could seriously increase that danger.

The newspapers accepted the situation and called off their cameramen. But one freelance photographer, clearly a founder-member of today's parapazzi, decided there was a lot of money to be made from being the only photographer to have pictures of the baby. And was out to get them. First of all he knocked on Eamonn's door and asked politely. Eamonn again explained why he had to refuse but the photographer did not appear to be impressed.

That evening Eamonn and Grainne drove off to visit friends, leaving Emma with a baby-sitter, and very soon Eamonn realised another car was following them. A few minutes later he was obliged to stop at a railway level crossing barrier and his suspicions were confirmed. The photographer leapt out of the following vehicle, pulled himself on to the bonnet of Eamonn's car, pointed his camera at the windscreen and started firing off frame after frame.

'That was in case Grainne had Emma in her arms at the time,' said Eamonn, afterwards. 'I felt I'd had enough of this man. I got out of the car and told him to go away. He ignored me and kept on clicking away. I felt my hand clench into a fist. I wanted to punch him. But somehow I restrained myself and instead I told him he was wasting an awful lot of film because we did not have Emma with us. Then a train started to go over the crossing and I got back into the car.'

Three years after they had adopted Emma came Fergal and, three years after that, Niamh, which is Gaelic for 'Morning Light'.

Having a family gave Grainne less time to become involved in Eamonn's life in television. It had never impressed her very much, anyway. Despite, or perhaps because of, her own show business background, she was never dazzled by the so-called glamour of it. She always appeared to prefer the company of the people who made up Dublin 'society' to that of the television 'celebrities' with whom she and Eamonn came into contact in London.

Equally, she gave the impression that she discouraged him from socialising with the people he worked with in television. Very occasionally they would entertain selected, long-standing associates of his at their Thames-side home, usually for Sunday lunch time drinks on the terrace which always finished promptly at two p.m. Seldom, if ever, did they accept a reciprocal invitation from a colleague.

Occasionally, too, they would entertain a member of Eamonn's programme team and spouse to a meal in a restaurant. But there the conviviality ended.

After a pleasant supper at a restaurant one evening with a colleague of many years and his wife, all four shared a taxi home.

It went to the couple's house first and as they got out they invited Eamonn and Grainne to go in for a nightcap. Eamonn accepted immediately and leapt out of the cab and started to follow them up the drive. But Grainne stayed firmly in the taxi from which she sternly called to Eamonn to come back. He mumbled an apology to the couple and did as she asked.

Very soon after he had taken on the responsibility of becoming a family man, Eamonn began to doubt his wisdom in turning down the American offer. Within three years of it being made, the BBC had axed both 'What's My Line?' and 'This Is Your Life', and he was out of a job.

It had not been because the programmes were no longer attracting viewers but simply because, in the estimation of some of the post-war Oxbridge bright boys then getting into positions of influence at the BBC, they had been running too long. Success was something the BBC did not stoop to in those days.

Eamonn who felt, probably correctly, that he was the target as much as the programme, was especially bitter because the coup de grâce had been administered by Donald Baverstock, who had been a driving force behind the pioneering 'Tonight' programme and was then deputy controller of BBC television.

Because, four years before, Eamonn had striven to give Baverstock's ambitions a boost by trying to get him the job of managing director of the new Irish television company, Telefis Eireann.

In his capacity as honorary chairman of the Statutory Authority, he arranged for Baverstock to be interviewed by his Board of Governors and listened with satisfaction as his protégé began to spellbind them with his fine Welsh oratory.

However, asked how he decided a programme had no audience-appeal, Baverstock seemed to overlook for a moment that the board were all church-going solid citizens, and included a retired, spinster schoolteacher, when he replied: 'I watch to see if it has an "S" point.'

For when another asked him, 'And what is an 'S' point?', he replied, 'An "S" point is the point at which the viewers cry, "Oh shit!" and switch off.'

Blushing Eamonn did not need the stunned silence that followed to tell him his boyo had badly boobed.

7

The chat show starts
and bedlam begins

It was a friend, Brian Tesler, at the time Programme Controller of the then ABC Television but who, as a BBC director, had worked with him on a few editions of 'What's My Line?', who came to Eamonn's rescue.

Like all the new commercial companies seeking quicky to envelope – or, more accurately, disguise – themselves in what some of their executives cynically called 'the veneer of the establishment', ABC had been anxious from the start to sign any BBC personality of stature and had approached Eamonn years before.

But with two very successful programmes beaming him into millions of homes each week he had spurned their offer. Now things were suddenly different and he was very ready to listen when Tesler offered him the job of chat show presenter – and a three year contract.

However, it was soon a matter for debate as to whether Tesler had done either of them a favour.

It quickly emerged that, as his friends had known for years, Eamonn was no natural conversationalist. When he tried it in front of camera the foot-hopping of which they were conscious was replaced by a more obvious combination of eye-darting and forced grins as he looked desperately for replies and reactions from guests which, frequently, were not forthcoming.

Worse, Eamonn himself quickly became sensitive to the fact that those silences he had never learned how to fill were embarrassingly exaggerated by television and as a result he anxiously tried to plug them with non sequiturs which, of course, made very little sense.

The result of these deficiencies on the guests was that the quiet stayed silent while the vocal simply grew louder.

Then, technique apart, he had prejudice to contend with. He became a victim of the tall poppy syndrome and many were out to cut him down to size. There was resentment and jealousy in some quarters of British show business, and sections of the press, too, that this Irishman with little evident talent should be handed this new prize on a plate. On top of that, many viewers – believing he was in a position to pick and choose his programmes – were upset at him for stepping out of the familiar avuncular role he had played for so long.

But his real handicap was that he had had it too easy in television, and for too long.

Where he was to blame was that he did not have the foresight to see that he would have to master new skills or, if he did, was too lazy or too complacent to make the effort.

With so much coming out at him from the opposing corner in his new career it was little wonder the former amateur boxing champion was soon being ridiculed as the Joe Palooka of the chat show. He was very quickly on the ropes and before much longer he was practically punch-drunk. It was to his considerable credit that he never allowed his handlers to throw in the towel.

Brian Tesler told Eamonn of the programme which had been developed, or, less euphemistically, plagiarised (I was principal plagiariser) for ABC from Johnny Carson's hugely successful 'Tonight' show on America's NBC network.

This programme was transmitted by ABC to the North of England and the Midlands late on Saturday nights and was fronted by a gentle character named James Lloyd, who later became pre- senter of a BBC radio Country and Western music programme and, although it always contained music and comedy spots, it was essentially a chat show.

So, when Eamonn let it be known, after he joined ABC, that the chat show he was starting was something completely new to British television, that had not been totally true, either.

The comedy element, which was in addition to interviews with local celebrities and any who could be lured to the studios in

Manchester, was a weekly sketch by the satire-and-pop-group 'The Scaffold', whom I had 'discovered' performing in an Arts Festival at Liverpool's Everyman Theatre. Later they were to become nationally known for records such as 'Thank You Very Much' and 'Lily The Pink'.

The programme laboured under the rather odd and very dull title of 'Gazette' but its ratings made it a jewel in ABC Television's regional crown and encouraged the company to try to find it a national network spot.

Originally, because they were looking for a presenter with a comedy background, which was reckoned to be one of the reasons for the success of Johnny Carson on his nightly chat show in America, ABC wanted Bruce Forsyth for the job.

But Forsyth, who had just finished compèring the programme that brought him national recognition, 'Sunday Night At The London Palladium', had no desire to become the Johnny Carson of Britain.

He already had ambitions – unfortunately still unfulfilled today after twenty-five years – to become the Bruce Forsyth of America. He turned the offer down.

So, although Eamonn was not the kind of presenter ABC had in mind he *was* a national name and he *was* available and Tesler offered him the job on the network chat show at the then phenomenal fee of £40,000 a year.

So he went to Manchester to see 'Gazette' for himself and it was then, early in 1964, that we met for the first time. It was a memorable meeting. The first thing he did was hand me a matchbox with a dead bug inside it.

I had wondered what to expect of the man who in the last decade had become one of the best known personalities in Britain, truly its first ever popular television star.

Despite the fact that, by then, I had come face to face with quite a number of the personalities of the day, none was as famous as Eamonn Andrews and I was a little bit overawed by the prospect of our meeting. So I armed myself with a few carefully prepared words of greeting, telling him of the honour I felt that he should take so much interest in the show of which I was editor.

But when he arrived at the studios and I delivered my brief but carefully rehearsed speech, Eamonn took no notice. Instead he fished in his jacket pocket and brought out a Swan Vestas matchbox which he thrust at me.

'Take a look inside,' he said. 'That bit me during the night at Manchester's poshest hotel. It's a bed bug.'

He was very serious about it, and was practically fuming. He explained that the bug had struck as he lay sleeping in the hotel's suite.

He was in so much discomfort he had to call the hotel doctor and was also so furious that, while the doctor was on his way, he ripped all the sheets from the bed, located his attacker, emptied the matchbox and immediately imprisoned it inside.

To ease the pain the doctor gave him an injection in his backside. But then came the real reason for Eamonn's fury. When he went to pay his bill the following morning, he found he had nearly been bitten again. A fee for the doctor's services had been added to it. He almost needed an injection to ease the pain of that, too. But he simply refused to pay.

Eamonn liked the show but not the Scaffold, whose humour only puzzled him. The following week Tesler told the 'Gazette' production team that it was to become a fully networked programme later that year but without the Scaffold and, of course, Jimmy Lloyd from whom Eamonn was taking over as presenter.

And the programme was going to have a new name. Despite the disaster 'The Eamonn Andrews Show' had been during its six-week run on the BBC not many years before, Eamonn still wanted an own-name show. So ABC settled for the eponymous title.

However, two months before the chat show even went on the air they began to get worried that they might have signed totally the wrong man. Eamonn's aloofness from show business, and much else that appealed to the wider television audience, hit them at the initial programme planning meeting.

The first object of the meeting was to discuss a pilot show which was to be more a full-scale dress and technical rehearsal rather than an exercise to decide whether or not ABC would go ahead with the programme as a series. It was too late for them, then, to change their minds about that; they had committed themselves too deeply to producing the show to pull out now.

The second reason for the meeting was to decide on four well-known, popular guests for the all-important opening programme and it was that part which brought the first real shock.

Two years earlier the situation comedy 'Steptoe & Son' had been launched and, at the time of the meeting, it was being watched, according to BBC figures, by 28 million people. So it was a fairly obvious suggestion of mine that we should invite Harry H. Corbett, who played the son, to be one of Eamonn's first guests.

The others agreed. But Eamonn looked unhappy at the suggestion and we all waited to hear what was worrying him. Eventually, to everybody's astonishment, he asked, 'If we have him as a guest, what will we do with Sooty bear?'

It took a few seconds for it to dawn on the meeting that Eamonn thought the person I had proposed was Harry Corbett the puppeteer and that he had never seen or heard of 'Steptoe & Son' or Harry H. Corbett.

In the silence that followed we looked to the man who had signed him to the chat show role to which it now seemed he was not going to be suited, Brian Tesler.

Ironically only eighteen months earlier Tesler – later to become chairman of London Weekend Television – had questioned the interviewing techniques of a newcomer named Michael Parkinson.

At my instigation Parkinson was then working on a current affairs show for ABC, of which I was programme editor, and Tesler had wondered if his 'laid back' style was suitable for television or if he should stick to print journalism where he was also working.

As it happened Parkinson left the programme of his own accord, but later, of course, became the most successful ever British chat show presenter with, at eleven years, the longest running talk programme to date thanks to that same interviewing style.

However, Tesler showed the greatest restraint the day of that first production meeting with Eamonn. Disguising the sense of incredulity he must have felt, he patiently explained to Eamonn that the man proposed was someone who was winning accolades for his performances in the most successful situation comedy of all time. He was not, he pointed out, the little man on tiny tot's television who wore a glove puppet resembling a small bear which he called Sooty and which he made to appear to squeak-speak such poetic couplets as 'Izzy, wizzy, let's get busy.'

He did not, however, add that, as had also been well publicised, the actor had deliberately put the H into his name – saying it stood for 'Hanything' – so there would be little danger of him being confused with the Harry Corbett the popular puppeteer. It was not the sort of thing you said to a man you were paying four times as much as the Prime Minister earned.

Although at that first chat show meeting Eamonn explained his confusion with the two Corbetts by confessing he had never heard of Harry H., he was persuaded the 'Steptoe & Son' actor would make an acceptable first guest.

But before that opening show came the pilot show and it was marred by tragedy.

Four members of a charity committee – one aged eighty-six, another the twenty-four-year-old chairman – who had taken part in the pilot were killed in a car crash on their journey home.

They were from Denby Dale, Derbyshire, where every twenty-five years villagers cook a giant meat-and-potato pie and sell portions of it to raise money for charity.

It is a tradition that goes back to 1778 when the first pie was baked to celebrate the recovery from lunacy of King George III (although two weeks later he was considered to be quite mad again).

The tragedy nearly reached scandal proportions. The other members of the committee claimed they only agreed the four men should make the 400 mile round trip because the member of Eamonn's production team sent to see them assured them the pilot would be transmitted and the charity would benefit from the publicity.

They said they were even more devastated when they learned this had never been ABC's intention.

In the immediate aftermath of the incident, members of the production team were surprised to discover Eamonn was far from being the compassionate, caring person their preconceptions had led them to believe. They discovered him to be the very opposite, a man able to snap shut his mind to almost anything, any emotion, that conflicted with his immediate ambition. It was their first insight into the toughness of temperament that had got him to the top.

He remained totally detached from the tragedy. Never once did he even mention it, nor utter a word of sympathy for the victims or their relatives.

Despite these unfortunate events, the first programme went ahead as scheduled, in October, 1964.

Among all the ballyhoo of its launch, the ABC publicity machine declared it to be an occasion on which Eamonn Andrews met 'The Sunday Night People', as they decided to call the show's guests, and for months afterwards the phrase 'Eamonn and the Sunday Night People' was used with every mention of the programme.

That is until one journalist was so inconsiderate as to ask Eamonn, 'What exactly is a Sunday Night Person as opposed to, for instance, a Tuesday Morning Person or a Friday Lunchtime Person?' and Eamonn found himself somewhat stumped for a convincing answer.

As events turned out, Harry H. Corbett was not available for that first show but appeared on the second. The final line-up was comedy actor Terry-Thomas, actor-cartoonist Willie Rushton – also unknown to Eamonn – actress Honor Blackman, and six times world boxing champion Sugar Ray Robinson.

Robinson was in Paris for a championship fight when the programme was being prepared and, with boxing the one topic on which Eamonn could talk easily, ABC saw this as a heaven-sent opportunity to give his confidence a much needed boost on the opening show.

So, at considerable cost, they flew Robinson and his entourage from Paris to London especially for the programme.

A very wise move it proved to be, too, because the only time Eamonn seemed at ease in his new role was when he introduced Robinson as his last guest.

One incident in the programme was to give the production team yet another glimpse of the kind of situation Eamonn was going to get himself into.

Just before he brought Robinson on he had introduced a then little-known singer named Sandie Shaw, who was to sing the song on her first record, 'Always Something There to Remind Me'.

But despite the fact that he himself had something there to remind him in the shape of a crib-card, Eamonn mysteriously announced that the song she was about to sing was called 'So Long As You're Happy, Baby'.

After the show the production team discovered he had put the card, on which the song title was written, in the wrong place and could not retrieve it. So, rather than admit he did not know the title he simply made one up.

Fortunately Miss Shaw went into the song as rehearsed, and while she was singing the programme director called Eamonn on the house phone linked to the desk from which he presented the show, gave him the right title and asked him to correct it when the song finished. Eamonn, loathe as always to admit to an error, at first refused, arguing that nobody would have noticed a mistake in something as trivial as a pop song.

Eventually, just as the song was ending, he condescended to make the correction. But when he did, he got it wrong again – although he was getting warmer. He told the audience that he should have announced the title as, 'There's Always Someone There to Remind You, Baby'.

This lapse – another quickly followed when he declared that the Duchess of Bedford lived in Woburn Avenue – was, the production team was to discover, more than merely an indication that he seemed to think it was mandatory for every pop song title of the day to contain the word 'baby'. It was also a warning to them that, despite how much his chat show was to depend on them for ratings, he was going to be as cavalier with music and musicians as he was with every other aspect of show business – even with musicians as massively and internationally successful as the Beatles had then already become.

On the programme for the Easter Sunday following the show on which they appeared – and on which he had kept confusing George Harrison with Ringo Starr – there was to be a spot featuring a large family of boys from their native Merseyside, all of whom had demonstrated remarkable academic ability.

Eamonn had the idea that to pay off the item he should present the youngest with a giant-sized Easter egg on which, he suggested somewhat naively and certainly optimistically, the programme should get the Beatles to pipe their autographs in icing sugar.

I was discussing this suggestion with him at his home in Chiswick that Sunday morning when the then producer arrived very late for the meeting, mumbling his apologies. Eamonn, a punctuality fanatic, simply ignored him and continued talking about the egg. The producer listened, puzzled. Eventually he tried to get in on the conversation. 'What's all this about an egg?' he blurted out.

Eamonn, who had not only been conducting the meeting for half an hour but had also been to Mass at seven o'clock that morning, glared at him, and eventually replied, testily, 'It may have escaped your notice but today happens to be Easter Sunday.'

The producer, who was Jewish, lapsed into silence again, but only for a second. Then, with a hurt tone in his voice, he said to Eamonn, 'I don't know what you're getting at me for. But for us there wouldn't be any Easter.'

Eamonn continued to ignore him.

Talented though they were, the Beatles not unexpectedly told the programme through their press relations department that their skills did not run to autographing easter eggs with icing sugar, nor did they have the time to master the art before that night's programme.

When Eamonn heard their reaction he was furious and as obstinate as always. 'Sod them,' he said, 'we'll get somebody just to write their names on it with icing. Just John, Paul, Ringo and ...'

'George,' said the producer.

'With a "Happy Easter" message,' Eamonn went on.

'But we can't really forge the Beatles' signatures,' I protested, 'and certainly not in icing sugar.'

'That's the very reason why we can,' Eamonn retorted, triumphantly. 'They're not going to complain and admit they didn't give a stuff for the kids, and the kids won't know the difference.'

So that night he presented the beaming youngster with the giant egg, pointing out the 'signatures' of each of the Beatles. And he was right. There was no complaint from the Beatles and the boys did not notice or if they did they didn't look a gift egg in the mouth.

When the production team met for an 'inquest' on the first transmission of 'The Eamonn Andrews Show', it wasn't, however, Eamonn's double-goof with the song title that topped the agenda.

The team was much more concerned that, as with the pilot, far too much of the programme had consisted of 'dead air time'. These were the seemingly endless intervals of silence which occurred as, between nervous laughs, coughs, and clearing of throat, Eamonn strained to read the next of his questions, all of which were typed on cards concealed on his desk.

He made the question-asking operation even more laborious because he also tried to give the impression that, far from reading it, he was actually conjuring up the question there and then.

Another worry was the discovery that, after he had eventually succeeded in getting a question out, unfortunately he did not then listen to the answer.

This caused a lot of problems.

A guest's reply to a question frequently pre-empted the next one on the cards. But, as Eamonn had not taken in the answer, he usually asked it just the same. This left the guest puzzled as to why he had asked him a question to which he had already given the answer and Eamonn puzzled as to why the guest looked puzzled.

He would have been totally lost without those question cards, however. All of them had to be typed in capitals and the words on his autocue, too, had to be printed in extra large type, because one of Eamonn's vanities was that he suffered from very poor eyesight but would never be seen wearing glasses. (Another was that secretly he used to smear boot polish on his bald patch before going in front of the cameras and, later, he used a spray which thickened the hairs and darkened both them and the bald patch).

Besides the questions, every single word he spoke in a show was also printed on the cards; his opening and closing lines, his introductions to the guests and each link-line between the introductions. The entire script, in fact.

He clung to those cards like the cartoon character Linus clings to his comforting blanket until the last possible moment, going over them again and again until it was time for the show to start.

Then, as the audience was filing in, one of the team had to stroll into the studio as though making a final technical check and surreptitiously hide them behind the desk telephone.

It was a responsibility none of the team ever wanted. Everyone had the nightmare that they would forget to put the cards in position one night and thereby strike Eamonn completely dumb for the whole of the programme.

He was so paranoiac about having access to every word he was likely to need in a show that when he was question-master of 'What's My Line?' he even had lines written on the backs of the numbered cards with which he kept the score. So, as he flipped one over each time a panellist got a 'no' answer, there in front of him to read were the lines '1 down with 9 to go', 2 down with 8 to go', and so on until there had been ten 'no' answers.

However, on one occasion he had both the panel and the contestant completely baffled when he misread an 8 as a 3 and announced the score as '3 down with 2 to go'.

Another aid he had on his desk during 'The Eamonn Andrews Show' was an egg-timer – one that had been specially made so that the last grain of sand ran out in exactly thirty-nine minutes and five seconds. Allowing for commercials, that was the precise running-time of the programme. Fortunately, getting out on time was something at which Eamonn was expert because he repeatedly forgot to invert the egg-timer to set the sands running at the start of the show.

Despite all the crutches with which he was supplied he limped through the first chat show painfully slowly and because of this and the fact that it went out close to midnight, it was immediately dubbed soporofic.

And, because it also appeared unlikely Eamonn would ever be able to give it the pace needed if it was to hold on to the size of audience by which the TV companies would judge its success, the show seemed doomed to immediate failure.

Clearly something very drastic would have to be done if it was to be saved. But, short of a miracle, such as the spirit of Groucho Marx suddenly descending on Eamonn, we had no idea what.

However, something did happen that turned the show into compulsive viewing and Eamonn himself played a major role in the events that led up to it.

But, in doing so, he also started a chain of events that was to turn him into the most derided performer on television; mocked as pathetic by some, a laughing stock by others, even a menace to the nation's morals by a few.

The cause of it was that he had a near sychophantic regard for titled people, perhaps because he was trying to over-compensate for the fact that he was born and brought up almost literally and figuratively beyond the pale.

It was for this reason that Lady Isobel Barnett was by far his favourite among the panellists of 'What's My Line?' in its BBC days, and, when Thames revived it, he tried to tempt titled people like Lord Lichfield and Lady Miranda Iveagh onto the panel.

It was certainly the reason he took a special interest when a researcher proposed the Earl of Arran as a guest for the second edition of 'The Eamonn Andrews Show'.

Some of the team regarded Lord Arran, who was called 'Boofy' by his friends, a rather pompous, silly-ass figure, who was likely to bore the viewers into switching off. But Eamonn insisted he must be invited.

The team cheered up a little, however, when they discovered how Arran described the way to distinguish the different ranks of the peerage from their regalia. For the description was more tongue-in-cheek than plum-in-mouth and sounded as though it might get at least a few ribald giggles from the studio audience.

The problem was how to make certain it emerged on the show without Eamonn banning it. If they gave him a question that would ensure it came out he would want to know what answer to expect. And, for all his naivety, even he would realise the answer was a little risqué and would therefore refuse to ask the question.

Arran could not spontaneously trot out the material they wanted, however, so the only way to set it up had to be with the help of one of the other guests, who, besides Harry H. Corbett, were actor Laurence Harvey, singer Petula Clark, and comedian Ted Ray. Ray was ideally suited for the job, so one of the team had a word with him before the show.

He agreed to co-operate, but what nobody realised was how Laurence Harvey, who had arrived with his own supply of vintage white wine and was not, of course, involved in the conspiracy, could turn the faintly risqué into the blatantly bawdy.

Midway through the show, with Harvey and Petula Clark also on the set, and Harry H. Corbett waiting to make his entrance, Ray asked Lord Arran the seemingly innocent question, 'When members of the peerage are all wearing ceremonial robes, how can you tell the difference between an earl, a duke and a baron?'

Replied Lord Arran, truthfully and with apparent ingenuousness, 'You can tell by the amount of ermine they have on their robes. And by their coronets. The coronets are like this: On mine I have four strawberry-leaf emblems ... and I have eight balls ...'

At this, Harvey jumped in with glee, crying, 'That's as many as we've got on this programme!'

This was greeted by an explosion of laughter from the three-hundred-strong studio audience, which Eamonn appeared to pretend he hadn't heard, and Petula Clark suddenly started to study the ceiling.

Arran pressed on, dead-pan, '... whereas a marquis has six balls and four strawberry leaves and a duke has only strawberry leaves.'

Then he finished with a flourish, 'In fact, a duke's got no balls at all.'

By now Harvey, Ray, and the audience, were rocking with laughter, while Eamonn, trying to disguise his nervousness by pretending to clear his throat, desperately searched for a way to change the subject.

'Talking of strawberries . . .', he suddenly interjected.

The audience exploded with laughter again and, with a huge theatrical gesture of helplessness, Harvey slipped off the settee.

But for the way Harvey had mischievously pointed up Arran's words, the whole episode might have been passed over as, at most, an innocuous bit of double-entendre. As it was, the 'phones started to ring immediately with viewers queuing to complain about Harvey's 'outrageous behaviour'.

Next day the press joined the chorus. Even though it was the dawning of the age of permissiveness they threw up their headlines in horror that such things should have been said on television and on a Sunday night at that.

And the fact that the programme was fronted by such a mammoth of moral uprightness as Eamonn Andrews of course gave the situation that much more piquancy.

It was, however, a considerable consolation to ABC Television that, with this massive publicity boost, 'The Eamonn Andrews Show' had just been born as a ratings-puller. But, equally, any hope that Eamonn Andrews would ever be considered to be a chat show host of any credence had just died.

The hullabaloo for the show to be cleaned up was to reach an even higher pitch and one which inspired cartoonist Jak of the London *Evening Standard* to caricature Eamonn introducing his guests for one show as Enid Blyton, the Archbishop of Canterbury, and Lord Hill then Chairman of the Independent Television Authority (later the Independent Broadcsting Authority), which several times warned ABC about the tone of the programme.

Eamonn might just have had a chance of regaining some stature on the following week's programme if the guests had been anything like as safe as those Jak depicted.

But he was out of luck. The principal guests for the following show had already been booked and they could hardly have been described as conversational conformists. They were the less-than-subtle comedian Jimmy Edwards, 'down-to-earth' Test cricketer Freddie Trueman and Sixties sex-symbol Diana Dors.

Very soon into the programme Jimmy Edwards steered the conversation to his famous eleven-inch-long handlebar moustache.

Then he said, 'A moustache is a sort of barometer of your sex life, you know...'

Eamonn braced himelf. And, up in the control gallery, so did we all.

Freddie Trueman interrupted, 'By the look of it you've got a heck of a long one.'

Jimmy Edwards pressed on. 'When it droops a bit it means you haven't had it recently', he said.

Eamonn struggled to get off the hook. 'Let me just talk to ...', he started to say.

Jimmy Edwards put him down. 'I'm talking to the *adults* now, Eamonn,' he cried.

And Diana Dors started to warm to the theme. 'Would you like me to give your sex life a trim, Jimmy?' she asked.

Eamonn, now visibly sweating profusely, made a desperate effort to get them away from the subject.

And, in doing so, he came out with one of the most bizarre introductions ever heard on television.

'Freddie, you've just been to Australia,' he said suddenly. Puzzled by this total non sequitur, Freddie Trueman just nodded. Eamonn stumbled on, 'I think everybody here has been to Australia ...'

Then with a weak grin he went on, 'This is just my excuse for bringing in a young lady from Australia, Miss Patsy Anne Noble!'

Patsy Anne Noble, a singer, who was waiting behind the scenes for the introduction Eamonn had so painstakingly rehearsed with her, was abruptly catapulted onto the set by a shove from an alert stage manager.

Then she was further stunned when Eamonn followed his odd introduction with an even odder question. 'Now Patsy,' he said, 'have *you* ever been to Australia?'

The singer stared at him in amazement. 'But you know I have,' she finally managed to stammer. 'I was born there. You've just said so ...'

In the control gallery the programme director hastily cued the opening bars of her music and Miss Noble went into her song with apparently the same degree of relief as Eamonn clearly felt at the prospect of a break from the racy conversation.

He also had reason to hope he would be safe when his next and final guest came on, because he was the celebrated, and somewhat more serious-minded, American screenwriter – of 'High Noon' among many other films – producer and director, Carl Foreman.

But, unhappily for Eamonn, Foreman made a casual comment about Trueman's career in cricket and Edward's penchant for polo and very soon the conversation again lurched towards the louche with the subject of balls again the high point with an occasional reference to the size of Diana Dors's breasts just to break it up.

However, by the end of the following week's show Eamonn really did seem to have established a break-through both to sanity and sanitization. Nobody had been rude, crude, or had told a near-the-knuckle joke. Eamonn's only frustration was that two of the guests, comedian Bob Monkhouse and Pamela Mason, actress wife of James Mason, who herself ran a chat show in America, insisted on disregarding him and interviewing each other.

This was to happen frequently. In fact at time guests took the show over all together. As he struggled to sort out his question Eamonn gave them plenty of time in which to do so.

Monkhouse, Mason, and the other guests, zany comic Spike Milligan and food and sports writer Clement Freud, later a Member of Parliament, later still an ex-Member of Parliament and a Member of The House of Lords, kept that night's conversation within bounds without being boring.

There was one tricky moment, though. Eamonn asked an American singer, Gene Pitney, who was filling one of the two music spots, what he did for a hobby and, innocent in his ignorance of English slang, he replied enthusiastically, 'I stuff birds!'

Eamonn, who laboured under the same linguistic handicap, was puzzled why this brought bawdy guffaws from both audience and guests. After all, as he said afterwards, it was perfectly clear that Mr Pitney was talking about taxidermy.

However, as the show neared its end, the chat was still crisp and, more important, still without a blemish.

So a relieved Eamonn went into a procedure on which we had agreed before the start of the series and which was designed hopefully to give him a tiny touch of the panache Johnny Carson put into his show. He made an on-air invitation to them all to be his guests again the following week.

So next week the programme started at an unusually brisk and very welcome pace and continued like that into the third and final part.

Eamonn was within minutes of putting under his belt two successive trouble-free programmes.

Who knows, maybe these two swallows would have made a summer.

But then disaster struck.

Eamonn had only himself to blame. In the days following his unexpectedly bold decision to invite the same guests to come back next week he had begun to worry that they would not be able to sustain fresh conversation for the whole show for a second time.

By the end of the week he was in such turmoil with self-doubt that he demanded the team find him a reserve guest; 'somebody interesting up my sleeve', as he put it.

The somebody eventually chosen was a professor of psychology, the theory being that as an authority on all aspects of human behaviour and motivation he would be able to talk wisely on *any* theme that arose.

And safely, too, said Eamonn.

So, unknown to the other guests, Professor John Cohen of Manchester University was 'planted' in the studio audience. As things were going so smoothly that night, Eamonn would have been wise to let him stay there. But he just could not leave well alone. It was his idea. He was going to show his clever guests – and the audience – how he could suddenly throw a surprise switch.

Minutes later he was wishing he had left it unthrown.

Without as much as a cue from Eamonn, the professor went straight into a largely incomprehensible diatribe on career women, the subject – inspired by Pamela Mason – that was being discussed. He droned on and on until Clement Freud suddenly interrupted him to say, 'Do you not realise that this show is either filthy or funny?'

Then, when the eminent professor pressed on by describing womanising men as 'a bunch of hymen collectors', Freud declared, 'Now you're getting the idea.'

Chivvied by this, the other guests, till then pristine pure through nearly two programmes, picked up the new mood. Between then and the end of the programme topics touched on included the mating habits of the hyena, activities in the conjugal bed, sex on the settee, Napoleon's love life, adultery, and sexual deviations.

It was one of Bob Monkhouse's earliest experiences of working with Eamonn and his observations of the way he reacted when his chat show made a sudden rush towards the risqué that night inspired him to refer to him when speaking of the winners of his show 'Bob Says, Opportunity Knocks' years later.

Said Monkhouse: 'We prepare them for anything that could happen in the business.

'We also warn them that they have to be prepared for the long, heavy sweat of show business. Or Eamonn Andrews as we call him.'

All that Eamonn managed to contribute to the rest of the show that evening was a weary, head-dropping 'Goodnight'.

8

Woody Allen comes face to face with Spike Milligan

Eamonn knew that, following the tone of the conversation prompted by the professor, he was in for another pasting by the press.

Most critics were purely derisory; almost all decided he was totally unsuited for the job. Said one of the more considered criticisms, 'Eamonn Andrews's apprehensive expression alerts viewers to the continual danger of overwhelming embarrassment.

'Traumatically, once a week, he lives out their social nightmares; an inexperienced host accidentally trapped in the public eye while he fails to cope with the emergencies created by hysterical, drunken, abusive or just plain boring guests.'

Said another, 'Eamonn Andrews is encased in an embarrassment which nothing can dent.'

And a third, 'If David Frost is the medium's arsenic, Eamonn Andrews is its old lace'. (He was also described as 'David Frost without blood').

Not surprisingly the press also spoke of renewed demands for the programme to be pre-recorded and edited before being transmitted.

ABC's hierarchy tried yet again to take some of the heat out of the situation by apologising to the Independent Television Authority and giving an undertaking that the programme would do all it could to avoid any further breaches of taste.

A more positive step they took was to issue an ultimatum to the production team that from then on the programme must only book 'safe' guests. These were to be people of stature who would never let a double entendre escape from their lips, or, more to the point, wouldn't even know what one was.

But who *were* these people precisely? Nobody could rightly say. Timidly the producer asked the management for guidance with just one example – apart from cartoonist Jak's unlikely list of Enid Blyton, the Archbishop of Canterbury and Lord Hill.

Eventually one was handed down by way of the head of the Features and Current Affairs department, under whose aegis the show came, and it made the production team blink. 'To begin with book Field Marshal Lord Montgomery,' we were ordered.

'Monty', the hero of Alamein, was a man not renowned for his affability and was then in his seventy-eighth year and living in retirement in the country.

But to my surprise, when I drew the short straw and had to 'phone him and ask him to travel up to London the following Sunday, and stay up until midnight talking on television, he was very amenable. It was only when I mentioned that the presenter of the show was a certain Eamonn Andrews that I heard what I might have thought was the death-rattle in his throat had he not added a strident 'Goodbye' as he crashed the receiver down.

We were just about to tell the management of Montgomery's lack of co-operation when we learned that something had just happened to make them abruptly change their minds about populating 'The Eamonn Andrews Show' with guests of that calibre.

That something was ratings.

Incredibly for a programme which was transmitted so late at night, in the graveyard of the week in fact, 'The Eamonn Andrews Show' had got into the 'Top Twenty'.

That was at the time media mogul Lord Thomson of Fleet, who owned Scottish Television, had just horrified the rest of the independent contractors by making the statement that was to haunt them for three decades – 'being awarded a television franchise in Britain is like being given a licence to print your own money'.

For ABC, having a programme in the Top Twenty between eleven o'clock and midnight on a Sunday was like finding another money printing press in their attic. They were not about to give it away.

Clearly the spectacle of Eamonn being teased and embarrassed and generally discomfited by his 'guests' was what was fascinating the mass of viewers, and they were prepared to stay up late to watch this weekly bout of bear-baiting.

But if it gets ratings, don't knock it. In fact, cherish it. That was the credo of commercial television and why ABC so abruptly replaced its instruction to us to book 'safer' guests with another which implicitly said: 'Ignore our last instruction'.

However, if, despite the close scrutiny of the ITA, they were not now prepared to spoil the spectacle by calling off the dogs, they must at least be seen to be trying to give the bear some claws.

Hence the memo to members of the production team urging them to try to improve Eamonn's on-air technique. As he had already been in broadcasting for nearly twenty-five years, attempting to improve Eamonn was a hard task to contemplate.

One thing that it was particularly difficult to legislate for was his inability to keep his composure when a guest said something to him, or to the audience, before he had managed to get out his first prepared question.

It was even worse when the guest asked *him* a question – it was usually on a recent newsworthy topic – before he managed to put one to the guest.

Guests often did this mischievously because they knew of his lack of knowledge of world events and that the question would leave him looking heavenwards for the answer.

It was also done with no malice aforethought by foreign guests, especially visiting Americans, who were out to make an immediate impact on the British audience. They knew nothing of Eamonn Andrews and presumed anybody running that kind of show would be a well-informed, man-of-the-world kind of person.

When these moments came, which they did very frequently, Eamonn again went through paroxysms of coughing, stuttering and grinning before he was able to get the programme back the way his cards dictated.

But by far the more difficult for him to handle were the guests who seized on the fact that the show was live as an opportunity to say or do something outrageous enough to get them a newspaper headline next morning.

They fed off not only Eamonn's well-known naivety but his much publicised religious convictions which had been even more emphasised only months before the start of 'The Eamonn Andrews Show' when he had been made a Knight of Saint Gregory, the Catholic church's highest lay order.

By the late hour at which the programme started, guests were often the worse for drink. It did not help that, even in those days, Eamonn, too, frequently drank more before the show than was prudent.

Except during Lent, that is, when in an act of penitential self-denial he tried to go the whole forty days without taking a drink or smoking a cigarette.

It did not improve his temper, of course, and to a man the production team rejoiced when he succumbed to his first cigarette, which he always did around the midway mark.

Another of Eamonn's idiosyncracies which made life difficult and frequently embarrassing for those who worked with him was that he made it a rule never to meet any of the programme's guests before the show.

He doggedly insisted that the first time he would meet them was the moment they walked out on to the programme itself.

It was a technique he said he had come across years before when he had appeared on a local chat show in California hosted by the country-and-western singer Tennessee Ernie Ford.

According to Eamonn, Ford would not meet nor chat to his guests beforehand, no matter how important they were, on the grounds that to do so would rob the programme conversation of spontaneity.

That may have been so for a more sure-footed performer. But Eamonn needed all the help he could get. In many, if not most, cases a brief chat would have forewarned him of how a guest was likely to respond to the planned topics, or of the guest's sobriety. Thus prepared he might on occasions have been less ill at ease.

Many guests resented Eamonn's refusal to greet them before-hand. Some saw it as a high and mighty attitude on his part and, because of it, were determined to bring him down.

Personally, I did not believe his reason for not meeting guests had anything to do with Ford – just as I also suspected the singer's strategy had more to do with the fact that he couldn't be bothered talking to his guests both before *and* during the show than it had to do with spontaneity.

At the time, I thought Eamonn was simply putting off the moment of confrontation for as long as possible because he was always out of countenance on a first meeting with people. Years afterwards I realised it probably had more to do with the social phobia about which I later learned. He frequently said he was much happier going out before a television audience of millions or a theatre audience of two thousand than walking into a room in which there were just a handful of strangers.

Whatever the reason, his rule caused the production team some embarrassment as we tried to explain it to protesting celebrities who expected at least the courtesy of a welcoming handshake from their host when they arrived.

It also led to some memorable moments.

One involved Bing Crosby. When Eamonn met him for the first time it was on the show itself and Crosby was, of course, wearing his toupé. But had he met Crosby beforehand he would have realised that he only wore the wig when he was in front of an audience – probably because he was an extremely careful man who saw no point in subjecting the hairpiece to unnecessary wear.

After the programme Crosby went to make-up and removed the toupé. Then I took him back to the hospitality room where the other guests, their relatives and friends, and the programme team, Eamonn included, were already having drinks.

For a while Crosby and I stood chatting close to where Eamonn, cigar in one hand, large whisky in the other – in later years he changed his tipple to gin – was in conversation with Bob Hope, who had also been a guest on the show.

After a few minutes Eamonn disengaged himself from Hope and came over to us. Then, to my surprise, he totally ignored the famous crooner but, within his hearing, asked me, 'Where's Bing?'

Furtively I indicated the shiny-domed, pipe-smoking character standing beside me. Eamonn, however, was now looking around the room and to my increasing embarrassment, he repeated the question.

I tried to make him realise with gestures that he was actually standing face to face with the man whom only half an hour before he had introduced on his programme as 'a living legend' but now did not even recognise. However, he still failed to understand.

Now he was showing signs of increasing irritation and I thought he was about to scream the question out loud when, to his amazement, the figure beside me began to croon in that unmistakable voice, 'Where the blue of the night meets the gold of the day ...'

And finally the truth dawned on Eamonn, whose face was now turning as red as the night in Crosby's signature tune was blue.

An even more farcical situation occurred when Jacques Tati, the celebrated French film director and mime artist, was a guest on the show.

Apart from being shown a photograph of him, Eamonn, who was no cinemagoer, did not know what Tati looked like. But what could have created even greater embarrassment was that, as he seldom visited Britain, Tati had never seen Eamonn before in his life, either. And, because of Eamonn's policy, neither was going to see the other until they actually met for the first time on live television.

When Tati arrived at the studios I welcomed him, introduced him to the other guests and discussed with him the form his contribution to the programme would take.

Came the moment, midway through the show, when he made his entrance. As Eamonn stood up and stretched out his hand to greet him, a strange look came into the Frenchman's eyes.

At first it was a look of puzzled bewilderment. Then it turned to one of near panic as Tati stared at this complete stranger who had grabbed his hand and, while vigorously pumping it, was talking to him in an accent even different from the others he had been straining to understand since his arrival in England.

Instead of letting Eamonn guide him into his seat, Tati stood his ground. He started to look wildly around, first at a now mystified Eamonn, next at the other three guests, and then at the studio audience, a few of whom were now beginning to laugh, as though they thought Tati had already started his act – perhaps miming a man who had stumbled on to a television show by mistake.

And because of the odd way the Frenchman was behaving, Eamonn was beginning to wonder if that really was the case. He was clearly unsure this was the man he had studied in the photograph before the start of the show.

As I was watching on a monitor up in the control gallery I suddenly realised the cause of Tati's bewilderment. He was looking for me.

I had forgotten to tell him this was the only television show this side of the Atlantic where the host actually stayed hidden from the rest of those taking part until it had actually begun. Understandably Tati had presumed the person who had welcomed him and discussed what he would be doing on the programme was also its host.

It was only after Eamonn had practically wrestled him down into his seat that Tati began to accept that he was the man in charge.

But Eamonn's troubles were still not over. He spoke no French and, in his confused state, Tati had forgotten what little English he knew. He could understand scarcely a word Eamonn was saying.

So, in order to cue him into his first mime which was to be a man playing tennis, Eamonn had himself to mime a man playing tennis.

Some time later, film actor Kenneth More was also to do some miming on the programme, with much less artistry than Tati, but with much more devastating effect.

It was to cause the ITA finally to order ABC to stop transmitting Eamonn's show live; to compel the company to tape it beforehand and, if necessary, censor it.

But before that unexpected display by More, Eamonn had to endure another session of embarrassment at the hands of Laurence Harvey.

At the time the first programme went on air, Eamonn naively announced – as did fellow Irishman Terry Wogan when he also became a chat show host twenty years later – that he would not have any guests whose sole purpose was to plug their latest commercial undertaking.

Very soon the production team was trying – and eventually succeeding – to make him face up to the hard fact that, generally speaking, the kind of guests that attract viewers will only submit themselves to the unscripted scrutiny and poor pay of the chat show if they have something they want to plug and are permitted to plug it.

Along with that, Eamonn had also to accept another home truth – and one Wogan, Aspel, Parkinson and others were later to learn – that there are not enough suitable so-called celebrities available in this country to fill many shows before repeat invitations – and repeated repeat invitations – have to be made.

Because of this, and despite his provocative performance the first time he appeared, Harvey was again a guest on the show a year later.

Not only was he on for a second time, he was there to plug his West End starring role in the musical 'Camelot' and before joining Eamonn for 'the chat' he sang the show's hit song, 'How To Handle A Woman'. Until then he was impeccable. But as he was walking from the music set to the guests' settee, he suddenly stopped to address the studio audience.

'I heard a joke today which I've just got to tell you,' he said. Then, with Eamonn defenceless to do anything but listen in dumbstruck horror, he proceeded to tell a very blue joke about the arrival of a train of camels at a Foreign Legion desert outpost where the men have not seen a woman for a considerable time.

Next day the newspapers were again full of outrage but this time questions were also asked about the show in the House of Commons and the ITA ordered ABC to apologise to the viewing audience for transmitting material likely to cause offence.

The Authority also made it clear that this was its final warning and it was one which was well heeded for a few months when little that was untoward was said on the programme.

But came the night when Kenneth More was among the guests and caught Eamonn completely off guard.

More, who was still being lauded for his portrayal of the legless flying-ace and war hero Douglas Bader in the film 'Reach For The Sky', very soon had viewers reaching for the 'phones, headline writers for the exclamation marks, and the ITA for the blue pencil.

Understandably Eamonn had anticipated only the politest of conversation from that quintessential English actor, but for some unaccountable reason he started cracking jokes about call-girl Mandy Rice Davies, who, with Christine Keeler, had been a principal participant in the then still topical Profumo scandal.

The giggles More's remarks got from the audience seemed to spur him to further attempts at outrageousness, and this time he made his target another much discussed figure of the day, rock-and-roll singer Elvis Presley. First he attempted to mime the gyrating, hip-swivelling actions that had caused Presley to be dubbed Elvis the pelvis; then he started to conjecture on the cause of the prominent frontal contours of the singer's tight-fitting trousers.

Eamonn knew immediately – as did we all – that he was officiating at his very last live edition of 'The Eamonn Andrews Show'.

He did not even attempt to protest at More's almost literal below the belt blows. By then he was only too aware that to do so would merely draw more attention to the transgression, or incite More to even greater attempts at outrage.

Next day's press was predictable. Several days later ABC ordered the programme to be taped an hour before transmission so that the sound could be faded or 'bleeped' when anything considered offensive was said.

However like a headless chicken the show still kept kicking after it had ceased to be live.

One of the guests on the first taped programme was fashion photographer David Bailey, who confessed to being very nervous of appearing on chat shows and had a few drinks before going on – although he is a non-drinker today. During the show he became very agitated as another guest was in full spate and suddenly yelled out 'Crap!'.

Considering all the sensitivity surrounding the show it was not difficult to presume the ITA would not be best pleased to hear such a word used on the very first censored edition and steps were taken to remove it.

An engineer was instructed to play the tape through and time the exact moment when it was uttered so that on transmission he knew precisely when to press the bleep button.

He got it wrong. On transmission the word 'crap' rang out loud and clear throughout Britain's living rooms and some inoffensive word that followed it was bleeped instead.

So again the newspapers had the shock-horrors. How unspeakable must have been the offending word the programme producers had bleeped out, they thundered, if they had left in such an outrageous one as 'crap'.

Eamonn was so furious about Bailey's behaviour that night that he never forgave him. Four years afterwards, when Bailey marked the end of the Sixties with a photographic chronicle of the decade called 'Goodbye Baby and Amen', Eamonn refused to be photographed by him for inclusion in it.

So determined were executives of ABC to try to graft onto Eamonn some of the panache they felt he needed if ever he was going to succeed as a chat show host, they engaged an adviser who years later was to have much more success assisting in the writing of the speeches which helped Margaret Thatcher become Prime Minister for a third consecutive term.

Antony (later Sir Antony) Jay had been one of the back-room team on the BBC's pioneering 'Tonight' and 'That Was The Week That Was' programmes and years later was to become co-writer of the very successful television comedy series 'Yes, Minister' and 'Yes, Prime Minister'.

He spent many hours at Eamonn's Chiswick home discussing the programme. But, despite ABC's optimism, unfortunately it was always unlikely that anybody with such ingrained gaucheness, as was Eamonn's handicap, could ever be changed.

By an odd coincidence, the behind-the-camera staff of 'The Eamonn Andrews Show' was to have another member who was also to go on to become a Margaret Thatcher image-maker, and also to be awarded a knighthood.

He was the show's second programme director, Gordon Reece, who was later to persuade Mrs Thatcher to make the changes in her delivery, hairstyle and dress, that helped her win the leadership of the Conservative party and consequently the Premiership.

Sadly, however, he was not able to do anything to alter Eamonn's entrenched image.

And, on their first meeting, he did very little to improve his own image, either. At least not in Eamonn's eyes.

It was also the first programme planning meeting that Reece attended and it was held at Eamonn's home. He arrived late which was a bad start to make with a man who was totally paranoid about punctuality. But Eamonn forgave his new director and after the meeting he suggested a welcoming drink for him, leading the team into his once elegant dining-room now somewhat spoiled by a gawdy cocktail bar, studded with dazzling mirror tiles, which had been installed at one end.

There Eamonn indicated a row of spirit bottles, attached to each of which was the kind of optic measure used in English public houses. Reece shook his head and Eamonn almost visibly rocked backwards when he said, 'I'd rather have champagne, please. It is the only thing I ever drink.'

Reluctantly, Eamonn opened the fridge and after some fumbling pulled out a half-full bottle which had been resealed with a champagne bottle stopper (the first any of us had seen).

By that time Reece had made a move none of us had ever before dared even contemplate. He had helped himself to a large Havana cigar from a box on the sideboard. And before Eamonn's mouth had finished falling open he was snipping the end with his own silver cigar cutter and asking for a match with which to light it.

The recruitment of those future knights – along with a team of experienced journalists and skilled technical people – was not the end of ABC's attempts to make Eamonn fit his new role. In a somewhat optimistic attempt to instil in him some of the wise-cracking skills that contributed to the success of the Johnny Carson Show, they next signed up a gag writer, Denis Goodwin.

Both as a solo writer and in tandem with his partner Bob Monkhouse, before he became a television performer, Goodwin – who, tragically, committed suicide while still in his thirties – had written for many of the world's top comedians including Bob Hope.

But though he could write the jokes for Eamonn he could never teach him timing nor cure him of his habit of giving a nervous cough before he delivered the punchline – if he had still managed to remember it. So Eamonn's attempts at comedy fell as flat as had the notes he tried to hit years before in his even more disastrous televised attempt to become a singer.

The company, however, would still not admit defeat or could not afford to. They decided that if Eamonn himself could not provide the humorous element they believed the show needed the production team would have to find somebody who could; somebody who would take a similar sidekick role that a character named Ed McMahon played on the Johnny Carson Show.

As a result, I went to talk to a promising young comedian who had just been in the West End hit 'Beyond the Fringe' – Dudley Moore.

When Eamonn discovered this was happening without him being consulted, he was furious. He was incapable of accepting his own failure as a funnyman and, in any event, he made it clear he doubted 'this unknown comic' would be a success as a regular on the show.

However, Dudley ended the argument himself. Sadly he turned his back on the glittering opportunity I offered him to make his name as Eamonn Andrews's sidekick – or even make it the 'Eamonn and Dud' show – and instead settled for his 'Pete and Dud' partnership with Peter Cook, and then a career as one of the highest paid stars in Hollywood.

Eamonn did, however, condescend to have him as a guest on his chat show a couple of times, on the first of which a young singer named Cilla Black gave him the name 'Cuddly Dudley'.

At that time, in partnership with Peter Cook, Dudley Moore had just opened the then mecca of the 'satirists', the Establishment club in Soho, and appearing there was a young, unknown comedian from Australia named Barry Humphries, who started to bombard the show for a booking.

Eventually I agreed but his performance as a chat show guest turned out to be a total disaster.

Afterwards, crying real tears of frustration into the long, lank hair that hung over one half of his face, he was almost paranoiac in his accusations that the fault was entirely Eamonn's. He claimed Eamonn had taken an instant disliking to him and deliberately cut him out of the conversation. The truth, however, was that Humphries did not exactly have a scintillating personality and appearing as 'himself', and without a prepared script, he was as tongue-tied before an audience as Eamonn could often be.

It was surprising, therefore, that two decades later the same Barry Humphries should have so much success presenting his own so-called 'chat show'. Not surprising, though, that he presented it not as himself but in his comic creation, Dame Edna Everage.

Another entertainer who had a traumatic time on 'The Eamonn Andrews Show' about then – it did tend to occur rather frequently – was singer Shirley Bassey. Traumas are, however, not unusual for that volatile lady who can often give the impression she lives in one permanently. But on that particular occasion it nearly led to a walk out by Eamonn's prized American big-name catch that week, actor James Garner, who was then starring in the tremendously successful television series 'Maverick'.

Miss Bassey, shedding more tears before the show than Barry Humphries did after it, was complaining about the scoring of her musical arrangement and threatening not to go on. Garner had never encountered Miss Bassey before and, unaware of her reputation as a tantrum thrower, assumed the role of the Southern gentleman gallantly protecting an affronted lady. He announced that if Miss Bassey did not appear then neither would he and, he reckoned, neither would the two other guests.

But one of those guests was comedian Kenneth Williams and when he told Garner, 'Don't worry, ducky, it's only our Shirl getting her knickers in a twist,' which the other guest, actress Dora Bryan, translated for him as best she could, he started to reconsider the stance he had taken.

Whereupon, Miss Bassey's resolution to go home quickly crumbled and she graciously consented to sing after all.

It was at the very end of that first year of 'The Eamonn Andrews Show' that the live television confrontation between Woody Allen and Spike Milligan, which was later to be much talked about, took place.

In an interview quoted in his 1985 biography of Woody, *Beyond Words*, Robert Benayoun quotes him as saying he had met Spike twelve years before, and adding, 'He's quite crazy and I love him.'

Woody's memory was faulty there. It had reversed the digits in the number of years, because it was twenty-one not twelve years earlier that he and Spike had met. And after that meeting there was certainly no sign that love was likely to blossom.

The memories of many of the people who witnessed the moment the two comic geniuses came face to face have played them false, too. They believe they saw Woody vanquished by a mad Milligan tirade. But that was not the case. Spike did it with comparatively few words and just a little clowning.

Nor was it, as some also tended to remember, Woody's first appearance on British television and his only appearance on Eamonn's show. In fact, Woody appeared on the show twice within three weeks in December 1964, the first of them in the week in which he celebrated his twenty-ninth birthday.

At the time he was working in Paris where the first film he wrote and appeared in, 'What's New Pussycat?' was being made. At the same time the LP of his nightclub act had just been released in Britain and, with the object of plugging both LP and film, he agreed to fly over to London to appear on the programme.

He had, not long before, also been such a success as a guest on 'The Johnny Carson Show' that when Carson took a holiday he had been invited to deputise as presenter.

When I contacted Woody in Paris and asked him to be a guest of Eamonn's I soon learned how the seemingly shy, diffident man to whom I was talking had achieved such success on a show on which the wit and conversation were supposed to be spontaneous.

His secret was that before agreeing to appear he made three important stipulations which protected his performance and guaranteed he got a lot of laughs.

The first really took me by surprise – certainly for cheek – but I was soon to learn the very sound reason for it. It was that all the questions he was to be asked on the show he must write himself. The trick was that he worded them all in such a way that when the host of the show asked them he was able to reply to each of them with the carefully honed jokes which he had tried out for months on the toughest of American nightclub audiences, and which were now also on his LP.

His second condition was that he must be the first guest to be brought on. This guaranteed him a solo spot and eliminated any danger of him being interrupted or upstaged by another guest while he was putting his stories across.

His last stipulation was that there must not be another comedian on the show. That was to make sure that it was *his* 'performance' that viewers remembered and equally important, he saw no sense in risking being the loser in any spontaneous battle of wits.

The only laugh Woody got from Eamonn, when I told him of the conditions he had made, was one of derision. He scoffed at the very idea of anybody, let alone a little known American comedian, making such demands. Moreover, he refused point-blank to have him on the show.

But – and something else Terry Wogan and the rest were also to learn – at most times, but particularly close to Christmas time when there are so many calls on celebrities' time, chat shows can't be choosers. When I got that message through to Eamonn he was finally persuaded to agree to Woody being booked.

The other guests on the show were Clement Freud and Dora Bryan, both re-bookings, and actress Tsai Chin, then fresh from the play 'The World of Suzie Wong' and projecting what she later called her 'Chinky-chinky Chinese' image with which she embraced so much of the East that on the programme, wearing the requisite scarlet cheong-sam split to the waist, she warbled her way through a song called 'Good Morning Tokyo'.

The show went well for Woody. Eamonn grudgingly but dutifully asked him questions about his childhood and Woody told of how he had been brought up in a neighbourhood that was so tough the kids stole hubcaps from moving cars – and other samples of the material from his LP.

But he further infuriated Eamonn when he ignored him totally as he gave his funny answers and addressed himself directly to the studio audience instead.

Eamonn was not very pleased, either, when later in the programme Woody had a chat with Clement Freud and Dora Bryan, in which he was not included.

Viewers' reaction next day confirmed that Woody had been a big hit on the show. It was information which Eamonn received with very mixed feelings. But it caused those of us struggling to fill the programme throughout that bleak month ahead to look covetously at the bands of funny stories on the LP which Woody had not had time to tell and make us want to book him for an early return.

We knew Eamonn would not hear of it. However, as Christmas approached, the only guest of any celebrity stature in prospect for the Sunday of the holiday week was a very tentative booking of revue star Beatrice Lillie. Weather permitting, she hoped to fly home to England for a few days seasonal break from her starring role in 'High Spirits' on Broadway.

That was still the situation at the start of Christmas week with more complications caused by holiday shutdown. So Eamonn, again reluctantly once more agreed to Woody's appearance.

Two days later, however, when we were about to book a well known politician to complete the guest list, Eamonn announced he had been having second thoughts about Woody's rebooking. He said he was fearful Woody's special kind of humour would not go down so well a second time and the Christmas show would be a flop.

Was he insisting that Woody be 'de-booked' then?

No, he had a better idea. We would keep Woody but book Spike Milligan too, and the show would be complete.

We could not believe he was saying this. He was as aware as any of us of the undertaking Woody had been given that there would be no other comedian.

And if he was insisting on another funnyman, why the zany,

unpredictable, uncontrollable Spike Milligan of all people?

The reason, it emerged, was that the night before, at Spike's invitation, Eamonn had gone to see him in a play in which he had just opened in the West End and in which he had a lot at stake. Spike was, of course, a long-time acquaintance from their days in the Joe Loss Band show and, as they chatted afterwards, Eamonn got the impression he would be grateful for a plug for his play on the show to attract the holiday time theatregoers.

I reminded him Woody had taken the precaution of making me promise to phone with the final line-up. If I had to tell him another comedian had been booked he would accuse of us breaking our undertaking and pull out.

But Eamonn argued that even if he did he reckoned Spike was a good swap.

In any case, he said, it was more likely Woody had never heard of a funnyman named Spike Milligan. By the time he found out who he was it would be too late.

I pointed out that he might find out about Spike in Paris from another ex-Goon, Peter Sellers, who was one of the stars of 'What's New Pussycat?'

But Eamonn's attitude, correctly as it turned out, was that by then Sellers would most likely be on his way home for the holiday. It was to become clear that really he did not want Woody *or* Spike. If he could get them he wanted *both*.

For sheer showbiz bezzaz so did I, of course. But I was also the one who had made Woody certain promises.

The real difficulty I faced with him was that it was not the names of the other guests he wanted to know, but what they did.

However, I realised – and I was later to feel somewhat shame-faced about it – that there was a chance I could get Woody to appear on the same show as Spike without actually lying to him.

That was because of the play Spike had just opened in. Through one of his bizarre career decisions he was playing the title role in an adaptation of a classical Russian novel by the nineteenth-century Russian writer, Ivan Alexandrovich Goncharov, with Bill Owen, Joan Greenwood and Valentine Dyall.

So when I phoned Woody that was all I told him about Spike, hoping he would not anticipate any ad-lib competition from some-body appearing in something that sounded so heavyweight as that.

What I omitted to tell him was that the play had opened at the Lyric Theatre, Hammersmith, under its proper title of 'Oblomov'. But the critics had not been sure what to make of it and despite Spike business was not good.

So, when he transferred it to the West End, he retitled it 'Son of Oblomov', and started to play it all out for laughs, involving the audience in typical fashion and ad-libbing madly through every performance.

There was just an outside chance that, even on the night of the show itself, I might get away with having misled Woody – I tried to reassure myself. Spike could be in one of two moods, totally zany or deadly serious. With luck he would arrive in the serious mood he is in when he wants to ventilate a topic important to him, like the environment.

From previous encounters, I had learned to tell just by looking at him which mood he *was* in.

If he arrived smartly dressed in a dark suit, he was obviously in his serious mood, in which case Woody would probably never appreciate the danger he had been in, and I would be saved a great deal of embarrassment.

Spike arrived wearing a red sweater and a woolly hat with blue and white hoops and a red bobble.

The first part of the show was almost a copy of Woody's previous appearance except, of course, that he used different material from his album. Eamonn asked him his own prepared questions about his unhappy marriage and he replied with the story about his wife being so immature she went into the bathroom while he was taking a bath and sank all his boats. And so on.

Beatrice Lillie was next on and Eamonn had a straightforward interview with her about her role on Broadway. But towards the end of it strange noises could be heard behind the scenes. Eamonn, Beatrice Lillie and the studio audience realised the cause but Woody was puzzled.

Finally, Eamonn introduced Spike.

The first television sighting Woody had of what he believed to be the star of classical Russian theatre was Spike shuffling in on his knees, still wearing his little woolly hat, and crying out, "Where's me legs! Where's me legs!'

Then, when he finally stood up, he started to wander around

the studio. This clearly began to unnerve Woody, who called out in alarm, 'Who is this man?'

When Spike finally did sit down he started talking in an incomprehensible Goon voice while a totally mystified Woody, who had now moved to the farthest end of the settee, sat and watched and wondered what had come over this person whose forte was supposed to be heavyweight acting.

Then Eamonn, who was getting no sense out of Spike, suddenly asked Woody, 'Did anything similar to this happen to you when you were in charge of the Johnny Carson show?'

Woody searched desperately for a reply to this totally unexpected question, then eventually shrugged and, stuck for anything funny to come back with, said simply, 'I stubbed my toe once.'

At which point Spike struck. 'I didn't know you smoked it!' he cried.

There was a great roar of laughter from the audience. Then, in his own mad-cap way, Spike pretended to apologise for scoring off Woody.

'Woody, I'll make it up to you in money,' he said. 'I swear to God I'll write to your mother. I've had too many to drink tonight. I'll shut up.'

Woody turned to Eamonn, genuinely puzzled by Spike's reference to smoking. 'Was that English?' he inquired.

Eamonn asked him if he had not heard the term 'stubbing a cigarette.' Woody said he hadn't.

Eamonn repeated it. 'To stub a cigarette,' he said.

This set Spike off again. 'Get the new, long cool, menthol toes!' he shrilled. 'Get cool toes today!'

Eamonn started to bring the programme to its close by asking Woody a question, but it sounded as though he was talking to a condemned man. 'Woody have you any last message to give the British public?' he said.

'Is the show over?' Woody asked.

Eamonn told him it was very nearly over and Woody replied that he had no final message. 'Just carry on,' he said. 'I'll be here dozing.'

He then curled himself into a ball and pretended to go to sleep on the settee.

At this, Spike burst into song. 'Just awearyin' for you ... ' he crooned, and Beatrice Lillie joined in.

Then Eamonn started to thank all his guests, finally saying to Woody, 'May I waken you to say "thank you".'

Said Woody, less than wittily, 'Eamonn you're so funny you make me wanna throw up.'

The atmosphere in the hospitality room afterwards was understandably, more hostile that hospitable. Woody and his two managers said a quick 'goodnight' and left immediately, not hearing the farewell remark Eamonn made which really explained why he had been so determined to have Spike on the programme.

Looking at Woody's departing back he said with a grin of self-satisfaction, 'That'll teach the bastard to try to take over *my* show.'

9

An Encounter With
A Call Girl . . .

Eamonn's wife, Grainne, frequently said of him, 'Poor Eamonn, he's such an innocent'.

It was a very accurate description. Eamonn maintained an almost childlike innocence all his life.

Considering the cynicism of the world in which he worked, many of those who were associated with him admired him for it and all of them marvelled at it. But it caused them problems because it was their instinct always to try to shield him from the realities of that world which would have offended that innocence.

That was something I found myself doing one night very soon after we became colleagues.

It was midnight in Mayfair. Half a dozen beautiful call-girls, most wearing very low-cut blouses and the shortest of leather mini-skirts, were draped around the richly appointed, softly lit room.

And standing right in the middle of them, drink in hand, was Eamonn.

That somewhat surprising scene met me when I arrived at the plush apartment for drinks with Lionel Stander, then a little-known American film actor who, years later, was to become best known as the butler in the successful American television series 'Hart to Hart'.

Earlier that evening Stander had been a guest on 'The Eamonn Andrews Show' and glad of the chance, too, because whatever Eamonn's shortcomings, the programme was regarded as a 'showcase' in which visiting show business people would be seen by British-based producers and directors.

After the show, Stander invited Eamonn and myself to his rented apartment for a 'night cap'.

It was very rare that Eamonn accepted such invitations but gravel-voice, six-feet-six Stander could be very persuasive. As I had some calls to make to America about the following week's show, they went on ahead and I followed later.

When I arrived I was first of all surprised to hear music and laughter coming from the apartment as Stander had not mentioned there would be other guests.

Inside, I discovered that apart from Eamonn the guests consisted of the girls and just two men, one of them a well-known hairdresser of the day, the other a pop group manager, both married, both without their wives and both of them dubious characters.

Clearly Eamonn had no idea what kind of company he was in and I immediately tried to alert him. But he was so unbelievably unworldly that had I whispered 'call-girls' or 'hookers' he would more than likely have thought I was referring to some kind of telephone operators or rugby players.

But finally he got the message that I was urging him to leave for some important reason and he slipped out of the apartment without any fuss on the pretence to our host that he was going to the bathroom.

Before I followed him out, I told Stander it seemed to me it was something of a naughty 'night cap' Eamonn had been invited to join him in.

Six times married Stander was amused when it dawned on him that such a long-time show business professional had not realised the exact nature of the company and would have been acutely embarrassed had he done so.

However, he insisted that he, too, had been surprised by the size of the party. He said he had invited his hairdresser pal for a drink after the show and, without telling him, he, too, had 'invited a few friends'.

He said he was not aware that somebody might have had it in mind to provide Eamonn with 'a little service' in the hope of getting him a return booking to the show because of its 'shop-window' value; something most little-known American film actors tried for.

As it happened, although he did not know it at the time, Stander did not need extra exposure, anyway. Film director Roman Polanski, who was in London at the time, had seen his appearance that night and had decided to cast him in his psychological thriller 'Cul-de-sac'.

Stander was genuinely surprised to hear of Eamonn's innocence. He had simply presumed a man doing his job would be unshockable, as did most visiting Americans who had never heard of Eamonn Andrews until their agents had booked them onto his show.

Among them was Robert Vaughn, then famous for his role as an undercover agent in the television series 'The Man From UNCLE'.

After he had been a guest on the chat show, he walked into the hospitality room with Eamonn, took one look at the female members of the production team and said, 'OK, Eamonn, who fucks?'

Flabbergasted, Eamonn just managed to splutter out the protest that he was not in possession of that kind of information (and certainly could not answer such a subtly put question with any guarantee of accuracy).

However, without the help of any pointers from Eamonn, Vaughn did date one of his researchers that night – and it was the start of a two-year romance.

But nobody ever told Eamonn that. It was not the sort of thing you did tell him.

A few years after his visit to Stander's apartment Eamonn had another encounter with a call girl. This time none of his colleagues could do anything to protect him – and the whole incident was almost caught on camera.

He was about to start a 'This Is Your Life' on former international footballer Joe Mercer, who was then manager of Manchester City football club.

The idea was that Eamonn would conceal himself in a phone booth in the foyer of the Hilton Hotel, in London's Park Lane, where Mercer was staying, and confront him as he was steered past by a friend.

The production team called the moment of confrontation 'the pick-up'. But, on the look out for customers in the hotel foyer that night was a call girl who had in mind a pick-up of her own.

And she tried to pick up Eamonn.

She spotted him as he tried to steal across the foyer to a line of phone booths, but she didn't see the hidden cameras as she sidled up to him.

Eamonn was about to take up his position in one of the booths when he was startled to feel a tap on the shoulder and hear a female voice say, 'Hello, you're Eamonn Andrews, aren't you?'

He turned to find himself looking at a very attractive, elegantly dressed young lady, and wondering if she was someone he should know. At first he thought she might be a film starlet he had met briefly.

Even when she suggested he might go with her to her flat in nearby Shepherd Market he was puzzled but still did not realise he was being propositioned.

He was even more mystified when she said, 'There's a friend of mine in the bar over there. She'll join us, too, if you like. You can be our captain.'

It finally started to dawn on him that this was no normal exchange of social niceties when she added, 'We'll give you the best time you ever had in your life, I guarantee.'

Although all the time he was terrified her intervention would ruin the carefully planned 'hit', as the surprise was also called, and subsequently the whole programme, he managed to keep outwardly calm. Politely he told her he would have to refuse her invitation because he had an urgent phone call to make and stepped swiftly into the booth.

Seconds later Mercer and his friend stepped out of a lift and Eamonn pulled off the pick-up *he* had in mind.

In the twenty-two years I worked closely with Eamonn I never once heard him mention sex, apart from when referring to the male or female gender. It was totally a taboo subject. You would no more discuss it with Eamonn that you would with a Mother Superior.

One guest on his chat show had reason to thank Eamonn for his censorious attitude, though. He was Leslie Thomas who was an unknown writer when I invited him to appear.

During the interview, Eamonn picked up Thomas's just published first novel, *The Virgin Soldiers*, and told 15 million viewers, 'This is not the sort of book you would leave lying around the house for *anybody* to read.'

Next morning, book shops all over Britain completely sold out of every copy they had.

One bestselling novelist who was never invited on the show was the American-born author of the *The Ginger Man*, J. P. Donleavy.

When a lady researcher returned from a press conference Donleavy had called to announce the London opening of the stage version of his novel, *A Fairy Tale of New York*, she told Eamonn she did not think he would consider him to be right for his programme.

'Why not?' Eamonn asked.

'Because', said the researcher, in a matter-of-fact tone, 'at the press conference I asked him if he had any unusual hobbies and he replied, "Yes, ma'am, fancy fucking!"'

Eamonn agreed. He could well manage without Donleavy.

Because of this heightened sensitivity to sex, or references to sex, the production team often even kept secret the identity of visitors guests brought with them to the show.

When convicted safe-cracker and self-styled wartime agent Eddie Chapman was a guest, he brought a beautiful young lady companion. Nobody dare breathe it to Eamonn that she was Mariella Novotny, the whip-wielding hostess of the notorious nude man-in-the-mask parties of the previous year's Profumo scandal, as it implied they had read of such lurid goings-on themselves and that was almost as bad as being there.

Even the sexual inclinations of playwright Joe Orton, there to talk about his recent impact on the West End with 'Loot', were kept out of his research notes, or Eamonn would have been unable to articulate his welcoming introduction to him on the programme. What also had to be kept secret from him was the fact that the man Orton brought with him was his lover, Kenneth Halliwell – who, shortly afterwards, was to batter him to death.

Gay people who worked with Eamonn daily, on both 'The Eamonn Andrews Show' and later on 'This Is Your Life', felt the safe and diplomatic thing was to keep the fact of their homosexuality hidden from him.

Though, naturally, they were happy to bring it out of the cupboard in front of the rest of their heterosexual colleagues, they quickly pushed it right back in again when Eamonn came in sight. He would not have known how to react to it.

One male gay who started to work with Eamonn on 'This Is Your Life' immediately after arriving at Thames Television from another company, managed to keep his homosexuality secret from him for ten years.

When he moved to London he did not give up his home in the country but, instead, made a round trip of more than 100 miles every day.

Eamonn, in his innocence, presumed this meant he was a self-sacrificing husband and father who put himself to the inconvenience of so much travelling rather than uproot his family and take his children from their schools. He spoke to other colleagues of his admiration of the fine example the man was setting and they said nothing.

Years after he had joined the programme the production team went aboard the QE2 for a 'Life' of her captain.

But as he relaxed at the party after the programme, Eamonn was puzzled as to why many of the ship's stewards were paying so much attention to that team member in particular and appeared to be well acquainted with him.

He asked another of the team and, perhaps because he was getting even more attention than he was himself, he would not be deflected from having an answer. So, as the QE2 sailed smoothly across the English Channel, another of Eamonn's illusions slowly sank beneath the waves.

A bad-tempered encounter with another member of the team, a researcher he had no notion was gay, once caused Eamonn to give a customs official the impression he might have been homosexual himself.

The researcher had gone to Paris to start work on a 'Life' of 'Madame Bluebell', the boss of the famous dance troupe 'The Bluebell Girls'. Eamonn, who was himself there on a brief visit with his wife, instructed him to return with them on the same flight to London so he could have a progress report.

Eamonn also had an important private business meeting in London that day, but the plane's take-off was delayed and he became both impatient and worried that he would be late.

He was already in a filthy mood when he and Grainne got to de Gaulle airport.

While they were waiting for a taxi outside the George VI Hotel

Eamonn had lit one of his favourite Havana cigars. But the moment he started to drive away the taxi driver who, of course, did not recognise his passenger, ordered him to extinguish it.

Eamonn refused but the driver said that unless he did he would not take them a metre further. So furiously, Eamonn flung it from the window.

'And then, to add insult to injury,' Eamonn told the researcher, 'the bastard farted!'

'Oh,' said Grainne, coolly, 'and I thought that was you.'

When the plane finally arrived at Heathrow, where a Thames Television car was waiting for all three of them, Eamonn ordered the surprised researcher to hand over his case for him to carry past the customs.

'We'll get through much quicker if I carry it,' he said. 'They *never* stop me. They recognise me and wave me straight through.'

He was, however, mystified when the researcher politely but firmly declined and by the time they reached the 'Nothing To Declare' channel there was almost a tug-of-war going on between them for possession of it. By that time Grainne had walked on ahead and out of sight, and Eamonn nearly boiled over when, as he had feared, the researcher was challenged by a customs officer.

No doubt thinking only of the meeting for which he was already late, he decided it would speed up matters if he intervened himself. 'This young man and I are travelling together, officer,' he said to the customs man, with a forced smile.

But the official insisted that the researcher must open the case. He looked inside, then he looked at the young man it belonged to, then at Eamonn. Then, casting his eyes to the heavens as though in disbelief, he dismissively waved them through.

Eamonn must have wondered at his manner. He had not seen that lying in full view on top of the clothes in the case that he had wanted to pretend was his own was a copy of *The Gay Guide To Europe*.

Despite Eamonn's narrow view of society's changing moral stances in the last decade of his life, sheer necessity compelled the 'This Is Your Life' team to start considering as subjects people he would have regarded – had he known more about them – to be representatives of the unacceptably permissive. And so working at the business of saving his blushes became an integral part of preparing more and more programmes.

That was why when they were working on the programme on Billy Connolly the production team did not tell him they had discovered the 'new-wave' comedian was having an affair with the outrageous Australian funny girl Pamela Stephenson. Not only would he have refused to have her as a guest on the programme, which they considered to be essential because of their appearances together on the comedy show 'Not The Nine O'Clock News', he would have cancelled the show altogether. So, apart from losing a very promising edition of the programme, they would have had the problem of finding another to replace it.

But they could not shield Eamonn from every eventuality and he got quite a shock as he described Connolly's courtship of his wife in a part of the script he had rewritten, as he frequently did, in his own elaborate language.

With his wife sitting beside him, he cooed to Connolly in his warmest of tones, 'Not long after you met, romance blossomed for you. And then you were married. ...'

'Aye,' called out Connolly, 'the tests proved to be positive.'

Eight months later he had left his wife, and was living with Stephenson.

Another time when Eamonn was diplomatically denied a piece of information about a subject was when the 'Life' of champion racing motorcyclist Barry Sheene was being prepared. A researcher managed to persuade George Harrison, a genuine friend of his, to make a brief film contribution and because of the ex-Beatle's reclusive lifestyle the production team considered themselves fortunate.

However, in it, Harrison jokingly referred to Sheene as 'a Midland Banker'. As it would have been almost impossible to cut the line out cleanly, and as the message was so brief anyway, they decided to leave it in but not tell Eamonn.

When it was played on the programme Sheene, as expected, burst out laughing. But Eamonn only gave a weak and puzzled smile.

Then, the moment the programme was over, he collared the producer and furiously complained, 'Nobody told me Barry Sheene once worked in a bank!

'There should have been a mention of it in the script. We should even have had somebody on the programme to talk about it!'

The producer simply apologised. He did not know how to explain to Eamonn that Harrison had been using rhyming slang, what it was rhyming slang for, and that it would hardly have been appropriate for a family show for someone to have been on the programme to talk about it.

To save more of Eamonn's blushes even the hotel accommodation made for programme guests was kept from him.

A booking request that gave even the highly experienced travel organiser a moment's hesitation came in the 'Life' of one of Britain's best known comedy actors when she contacted his wife to enquire what hotel arrangements she should make for after the show.

Said the wife, 'I'd like you to book one room in my name ... and one in my boyfriend's name.

'Then, after the show, I'll send my husband to my boyfriend's room but with *his* boyfriend. My boyfriend will stay with me in my room, and the hotel will be none the wiser.'

Then she had an afterthought and for a moment the girl wondered if she was now having misgivings.

But the wife went on, 'Come to think of it, you had better book a third room – for my boyfriend's wife. I don't think she should be left out.'

So, after the show, the 'subject' stayed the night with his boyfriend, while his wife was in the next room with her boyfriend and her boyfriend's wife slept in the room next to that. But not a word of it to Eamonn, of course.

However, it was one thing for his colleagues to be on their guard against saying something that might upset Eamonn's sensitivities, but a much more important problem they had was trying to keep Eamonn, himself, from saying the wrong thing on air.

This applied mostly to his chat shows, of course, and one of the principle reasons it happened was because of his habit of looking at his next question instead of listening to how his guest was answering the one he had just asked.

It was a nervous habit and the more nervous a guest made him feel the more he was likely to do it. World heavyweight boxing champion Muhammad Ali made him *very* nervous. So it was almost inevitable that he would give his most memorable display of it when

I managed to persuade Ali to make his first-ever appearance on British television on 'The Eamonn Andrews Show'.

It was the night after Ali had retained his title in a gory encounter with Britain's Henry Cooper at Arsenal's football stadium and the other guests I had booked were Noel (later Sir Noel) Coward, Dudley Moore, American comedienne Lucille Ball, American comedian Rodney Dangerfield and the singing group 'The Supremes' with a then unknown lead singer named Diana Ross.

Only months before the fight Ali had changed his name from Cassius Marcellus Clay for religious reasons. It was a move which had caused him to be the subject of a lot of derision which he had countered by declaring that he would henceforward acknowledge no other name than Muhammad Ali. The first thing Eamonn asked him on the programme was if it annoyed him when people still called him Cassius.

Ali said he did not mind when 'the ordinary person in the street' did so. 'However,' he went on, 'on some programmes in America, mainly in the southern states, some of them are rather smart and they seem to be looking for trouble. You know – how do you do Cassius, old boy! I tell them, "You know my name, fella!"'

And at precisely that point, Eamonn interjected to say, unbelievably, 'Fair enough. But let's have a word about the fight last night, Cassius ...'

The audience and the other guests were scarcely able to believe their ears. Noel Coward winced, Dudley Moore pretended to duck and Lucille Ball gave perhaps the first ever unrehearsed display of her famous look of startled, pop-eyed amazement. Everybody else in the studio practically held their breath wondering what was going to happen next.

However, without even glancing at Eamonn, who had now realised his faux-pas and was grinning nervously, Ali merely corrected him. 'Muhammad', he said, quietly.

It is not likely that Ali bore Eamonn a grudge for the events of that night but anybody who saw a contribution he made to, 'This Is Your Life' programme years later would have been forgiven for thinking so.

However, his efforts to make Eamonn look foolish were foiled by one of the many tricks Eamonn himself introduced which made the transmitted programme look the way *he* wanted it to look – and that was frequently very different from the programme that had been recorded.

But all those shenanigans were still very much in the future. For the present his immediate concern, apart from the bad notices he continued to get for 'The Eamonn Andrews Show', was the new image of himself he was trying to launch in the middle of the so-called Swinging Sixties as anchorman on a new sports programme ABC had just started for the ITV network.

Sadly, though, the Swinging Sixties seemed determined to go swinging along right past him.

10

Another 'Life' begins
and skeletons
cascade from cupboards

From the inception of Independent (its successful euphemism for commercial) Television in 1955, no company had rushed to undertake the potentially mammothly expensive, and possibly little rewarding, responsibility of providing the network with a sports service.

However, when they signed Eamonn, who had then been fronting 'Sports Report' for more than a decade, ABC were now prepared to take on the task.

At first, however, they came across numerous technical and contractual obstacles which led to delays and cancellations and it was not until the year after the Sunday night chat show started that Eamonn began his Saturday job, too.

By then his persona had been further punctured by newspaper comments such as one that described him as 'a fan so unsophisticated he would send for Andrew Cruickshank (Dr Cameron in the series Dr Finlay's Casebook) if he were sick'. So he decided he would use the new programme to try to create a new public image for himself.

Despite Grainne's declaration after they married about how he would dress from then on, as far as fashion was concerned he still seemed to be petrified in the Fifties. Now he was determined to change all that.

So he took himself off to a tailor in Savile Row and they agonised over it for a very long time.

Finally, when ABC's new 'World of Sport' was eventually unveiled, so was Eamonn's brave 'new look'.

It was certainly eye-catching. For there he sat in a blinding russet and black check, waisted and flared jacket which had no collar or lapels but, in their place, a narrow edging at the front.

So, instead of looking like a stylish new fashion, the jacket merely looked unfinished, as though it was one of the things there had not been time to complete in the final last minute rush to get the long delayed programme on the air.

The effect of it all was so startling that ABC engineers could have been forgiven had they screened the caption, 'Do not adjust your set, the interference is only temporary.'

And temporary it was, too. So fierce were viewers' reactions that Eamonn quickly restored normal service by donning his normal attire and instead of becoming a leader of fashion he did for the lapel-less jacket what Isadora Duncan did for the long scarf. Later he was to complain ruefully about the injustice of having to fork out more for a jacket without a collar and lapels than he had ever been obliged to pay for one which had them.

The two things were purely coincidental, of course, but shortly after Eamonn launched 'World Of Sport' the ITA decided it was time to take a look at its own image and make some changes in the structure of commercial television. So the members of the Authority put their heads together and, true to the tradition of committee planning, they set out to create a horse and came up with a camel.

The immediate effect on Eamonn of the new companies structure was that the ITA forced a merger between ABC, which had the weekend contract for the North of England and the Midlands, and Rediffusion, which had the contract for weekdays in London. Together they became Thames Television, responsible for weekdays in London.

ATV, which formerly had the weekend London contract, was forced out to the Midlands, but on a seven-day contract, while the new London Weekend Television company took over their London weekend hours.

So now Thames, controlled by ABC people who had many years of weekend programme expertise, had to start producing programmes for the weekday. Unfortunately, by the very nature of its content, 'The Eamonn Andrews Show' had always been a weekend programme, in fact a Sunday night programme.

Despite this, however, the company decided to try it out – for its fifth year – on Thursday nights. Now it was really doomed because it quickly started to lose the one thing it had going for it, ratings. The 'names' for whom the viewers had switched on had come principally from the world of film or theatre. They were available on Sundays, their one day off in the week. Thursday was different.

Meaningless though it had been, 'Sunday Night People' had a tiny, albeit tinny, ring about it. But 'Thursday Night People'?

Although the conversation had seldom been brilliant there had been a sort of fascination for viewers in seeing internationally known Hollywood stars 'being themselves'. Even if 'themselves' were abysmally boring.

Like Lee Marvin and Burl Ives (who did not even bother to take his overcoat off before he came on) who said practically nothing; or Jerry Lewis and Phil Silvers who talked for ten minutes nonstop and also said practically nothing. (In 1978 Burl Ives was brilliantly cast in the film 'Just You And The Kid'. He played a character who, for psychological reasons, was unable to speak.)

Now such 'glamorous' names were seldom available, a feeling of desperation started to grip the production team. And with it came the cries so often heard in television backrooms when there is nothing else left to say of a production running out of life.

'Let's take the show on the road ... What we need is a change of location ... a theme ... a freshness,' they cry. When what they really need is a rest.

So we took it to stately homes, to hotels, theatres, museums, provincial nightclubs. We even took it to a cave, a cold, dank, echoing place at Chislehurst in Kent, which gave the ever-griping sound people the first really genuine reason for complaint I ever heard them make.

It was Halloween and we filled the cave with witches and warlocks and a man wearing a leopard skin and leading a real live leopard on a chain. It was practically toothless and clawless we were assured, but the audience trapped in the cave did not know that when the man, wearing its brother's cast-offs, casually walked it among them.

But why a cave? And why a man with a leopard? I can't

remember now but it was probably because we had run out of stately homes and nightclubs.

One night the dying show gave a final reflexive kick. It was shortly after the musical 'Hair!' opened at London's Shaftesbury Theatre.

As this was the show in which moving naked people, both male and female, could be glimpsed for the first time on a public stage in Britain – depending on the skills, or whims, of the lighting men – we decided that putting Eamonn among them would raise an eyebrow, or even a hackle or two, among our slumbering audience.

It certainly raised the ire in Eamonn. We had, of course, expected that and we assured him that, despite all he might have heard, the part of the show we would transmit would be reasonably chaste and, while they sat around him on the stage for the 'chat', before ending the programme with the show's finale, the cast would be decently covered.

What we didn't point out, although no doubt he guessed it, was that to have Eamonn Andrews of all people tied in with such tittilation was going to get the show back in the headlines.

That certainly worked, but it was two of the guests, comedian Peter Cook and much-married actress Zsa Zsa Gabor, who really made the headlines the day after.

Cook had been invited because 'Hair!' was a 'hip' show and he was, then, a 'hip' person. The excuse given for Gabor's presence was that she had seen the show's controversial start in the States and could comment on it. The truth was that she was a 'name', was in London and was available.

In the event what they talked about had little to do with 'Hair!' – although, so to speak, it certainly made the hair fly – or about the peace and love the show spoke of.

Hoping for an amusing note to go out on as the chat came to an end, Eamonn went for the old how-would-you-sum-up question, asking Peter Cook how he would sum up Zsa Zsa Gabor, who was sitting within two feet of him, cuddling a white cat she had acquired to take back with her to America. Dangerously, not really meaning it, Eamonn added, 'Truthfully now.'

Zsa Zsa glowed in anticipation of the coming compliments as Cook first lit a cigarette. Then he looked her straight in the eye and said slowly, 'How would I sum up Miss Gabor? I think she's vain, has no talent and is a total non-event.'

For one of the few times in her life Zsa Zsa was almost speechless. Eventually she stammered, 'How can you say such things? You are the rudest man I have ever met.'

Cook shrugged. 'I was asked to speak the truth,' he said.

Recovering, Zsa Zsa skipped the remark about her vanity and went straight to the important part. 'How dare you say Zsa Zsa has no talent! Do you know they pay me $150,000 a picture!'

Cook was unimpressed. 'That's not necessarily an indication of talent,' he said.

Eamonn was wondering what had gone wrong again and how he could get out of this one when Zsa Zsa tried to drag him back in.

'Dollink, who is this man?' she appealed to him. 'Why do you allow him to speak to me like this?'

But to Eamonn's relief she then cancelled the questions. 'Don't tell me, dollink, I don't want to know,' she said.

And as Cook started on a fresh assault, telling Zsa Zsa that having brought the cat under the television lights she was certainly no animal lover, Eamonn managed to cue the cast of 'Hair!' into a song about sympathy and understanding.

Zsa Zsa was so furious she left London first thing the following morning and headed back to California. There she held a press conference at Los Angeles airport at which she said at much greater length what she thought of Cook, and so the new controversy about 'The Eamonn Andrews Show' went on for a day or two longer.

But, in fact, the cast of 'Hair!' had also sung the programme's swan song. A short time afterwards, Irish writer and diplomat Conor Cruise O'Brien was a guest of the show. He was in the wings listening to the conversation during the first part, waiting for Eamonn to cue him on during the second, when he suddenly got bored with the whole thing, changed his mind about going on and went back home instead.

A lot of people were now beginning to feel like that about 'The Eamonn Andrews Show' and, sadly, most of them were viewers.

The company decided to take the show off the air three months early that season and the last one was transmitted from the Cafe Royal on April 3, 1969. It was not a bad valedictory guest list, though – Yehudi Menuhin, Jack Benny, Yoko Ono and John Lennon.

That summer Thames sent one of their executives to see if he could find another programme for Eamonn in America where 'What's My Line?', 'This Is Your Life' and the 'blueprint' of 'The Eamonn Andrews Show' had come from, because, apart from anything else, he still had a year of his second three-year contract to run.

In the meantime it occurred to me that when he had first started to present 'This Is Your Life' at the BBC fourteen years before, I did not even possess a television set. And nor did millions of others. In addition, millions more who were then doing their courting in the back row of the local cinema had since married, had families and were now television watchers.

So, apart from all the programme's old fans, it seemed to me there was a potential new audience of millions of more viewers for a revival of it.

Another major factor was that colour, which would add an important dimension to such a programme, was about to come to commercial television. I suggested to Eamonn he should persuade Thames to give it a try, adding somewhat facetiously that a new version could be called 'This Is Your Colourful Life'.

At first Eamonn was bemused. 'But people will say it's old hat and have a go at me for not being able to come up with anything new,' he protested.

I suggested he think it over – and twenty-four hours later he decided he liked the idea. Within another twenty-four hours, having first seriously tried to sell it to them with the joke 'This Is Your Colourful Life' title – I was later amused to learn – he had persuaded Thames to like it, too.

It was fortunate for Eamonn that he did. Not only because their emissary to the States did not come across any other programme suitable for him, but by returning to familiar territory, to the safety of a script (which gave him back a great deal of confidence) he not only saved his career but ensured it would be financially successful until his death eighteen years later.

The BBC had the idea of reviving 'This Is Your Life', with Cliff Michelmore as presenter, a few years after he had gone over to commercial television. But, according to Eamonn, the idea failed because they overlooked the fact that when he had licensed to them the rights to produce the programme, which he had personally acquired from its creator, Ralph Edwards, he had included a clause that it must be fronted by nobody but himself (although Michelmore claimed he, in fact, turned down the chance to revive the show at the BBC).

However, when I suggested the Thames revival I asked him if he *still* had the rights, but he avoided giving me a direct answer.

After that I did not see him for about ten days and when I did I repeated the question.

'You *have* got the rights, haven't you?' I asked.

He grinned. 'I have *now*,' he said.

He explained that his lien on the rights to the programme had finally expired not long after the BBC had made their abortive attempt to revive it. But, as he saw no point in continuing to pay for something no longer of any apparent value to him, he trusted the BBC would remain unaware of this, and had not renewed it.

So, as soon as Thames had told him they wanted to go ahead, he had taken a plane to California and got the rights back again. Eventually, of course, Thames Television would repay him the fee he paid the Ralph Edwards organisation.

Once they had agreed to go ahead with it, Thames debated whether to start the programme at the beginning of the autumn schedules in September or to wait until the introduction of colour in November.

Fortunately for two young Fleet Street journalist friends of mine, Thames decided to wait until November and colour.

As programme consultant – I had turned down Eamonn's request to work exclusively as its producer because by then I was also writing comedy and drama scripts – I had promised them both jobs as writer-researchers on the show.

But in September they had both been incarcerated in a Spanish jail – having been arrested by police in the course of an innocuous holiday jape. They had, however, managed to regain their freedom in time for the November launch.

So they were able to go to work on the new 'This Is Your Life' and it was to be the first, and most vital, stepping stone in their very successful television careers. One, Jack Crawshaw, eventually became the programme's producer and also a television and film director. The other, John Stapleton, was to go on to become a reporter with 'Panorama' and 'Newsnight' and to present both 'Breakfast Time' and, with his wife, Lynn Faulds Wood, the highly regarded consumer programme, 'Watchdog'.

However, if it had been through me that John had got his start in television, Eamonn was responsible, albeit unwittingly – and with a little further help from myself – for his success in front of the camera.

Although he had come into television on a show which was considered to be 'Light Entertainment', John was still more interested in serious journalism and he soon got himself transferred to a writing job on Thames Television's regional news and current-affairs show, 'Today', which Eamonn was then also fronting.

But because he had not been consulted about the switch – sensibly because he was so possessive about 'This Is your Life' that he would almost certainly have blocked it – Eamonn over reacted and decided it had been an act of disloyalty.

He was so furious, in fact, that he soon started complaining about John's work to the producer of 'Today' and told him he would prefer him to be moved off the programme altogether.

But, as I had been largely instrumental in getting John his start in television, the 'Today' producer, Andy Allan, later Director of Programmes at Central TV, decided to consult me. And, having known John for years as a very able and personable news-reporter, I suggested he should be tried out in that capacity. I felt sure he would be a success as a television reporter and, in any event, it would keep him out of Eamonn's way.

John was, in fact, such a success on screen he was soon invited to become Eamonn's rival by taking on exactly the same job as his for the BBC's London news programme.

The Thames revival of 'This Is Your Life' started with a programme that was transmitted live from the stage of the London Palladium on November 19, 1969 – and almost with a disaster.

The subject was comedian Des O'Connor, who was topping the bill there. While he waited to go on stage to start the act Eamonn was going to interrupt with his book, he decided to step out of the stage door for a breath of air. As he did so, he saw a coach standing at traffic lights at the end of the street, about fifty yards away.

Then, as he looked closer at it, he thought the passengers seemed somehow familiar. He blinked and took a few paces towards it to try to get a better look at them. But at that moment the lights changed and it drove off.

Later, however, he was to realise he had just been looking at a coachload of his family and friends being driven to a hotel conveniently near the theatre. Half an hour before it started, he had, in fact, been within seconds of getting a clear view of every single 'surprise' guest the production team had gathered together, from several parts of the world, to make him gasp with amazement and move him to tears on their first big opening programme.

Researchers working on that first 'This Is Your Life' discovered O'Connor had been married before, and had a daughter from that marriage. Although the daughter was, naturally, very important in O'Connor's life, when Eamonn was told about her he said she represented what he called 'a jarring note' in the story and must not be included in the programme, nor even mentioned.

O'Connor was later understandably very upset and critical of Eamonn for taking this high-handed attitude. However, as the series progressed, unexpected discoveries such as that became common occurrences.

Frequently, though, unlike O'Connor and his 'unknown' daughter, they were the kind of very private matters subjects would have been very disturbed to learn programme researchers had come across.

Often these discoveries caused researchers themselves to have doubts about the ethics of the job.

A veteran researcher expressed how he felt about it at one meeting at which the 'Life' of actor Peter Davison was being discussed.

Davison was appearing in the television series 'All Creatures Great And Small', based on the books about life in a North Yorkshire veterinary practice.

When it came to his turn to report on his progress the researcher assigned to it, a comparative newcomer, said with distaste, 'Do you know, that when he delivers a calf a vet has to put his hand right up the cow's arse? Imagine that! He shoves his arm in shit right up to his shoulder!'

'Mm,' said the veteran without a flicker. 'Just like being a researcher on "This Is Your Life"'.

The programme discovered well-known people, including a famous war hero and an equally famous sportsman, who were not in fact married to the partners long believed to be their wives or husbands; subjects, such as a soap opera star and a celebrated dancer, who turned out to be illegitimate, or, as with one famous comedian, had police records.

Then there was the 'agony aunt' whose early life had been such agony her brother and sister refused to allow the public to hear it on the programme. Researchers found out, too, that a champion sportswoman was being persecuted by poison pen letters and also came across good reason to suspect they were the work of another famous sporting figure. Plans for that show were cancelled as were those for one on a well-known 'heroine' when the researchers discovered she frequently practised troilism and a young man she had seduced into joining in these activities had not long before committed suicide.

Searching for a 'long lost son' of a prominent woman social services worker researchers found the reason he was long lost was that for years he had been a fugitive from police in Australia who were hunting him for a serious crime he had committed shortly after emigrating there – a state of affairs of which his mother was totally unaware.

Researchers discovered that one of the country's best-known funnymen had completely falsified his war record and turned himself into a hero by awarding himself a number of medals to impress the woman he had married and who was still unaware (they let her remain so) what an uneventful war he really had.

And, looking into the life of one of the most distinguished broadcasters of the past three decades, whose pedigree was naturally presumed to be impeccable, they came across the information that the man he had always believed to be his father – and still does – was not, in fact.

Before and after he was born, the broadcaster's mother, a woman of the highest standing among their county set, was having an affair with her husband's 'best friend' and it was he who was the real father.

One of the most staggering and unexpected discoveries was made not before, but the day following a programme.

An angry viewer telephoned to complain that two 'actresses' –

one specially flown from Australia – brought on to surprise the subject of that programme were in fact prostitutes to whom she had once innocently rented a flat and whom she had consequently had to have evicted.

Worse was to come. When researchers tried to check out the viewer's claim they found out not only was it true but the girl they had flown from Australia was using the luxury hotel, where the programme was paying for her accommodation for the best part of a week, as a base for a spell of soliciting while she was in London.

Then there were 'This Is Your Life' programmes in which the team suspected a wife had co-operated only because she hoped the sentiment and nostalgia generated by it would cause a failing marriage to be saved. And programmes they suspected had caused a marriage to come to an end – or certainly accelerated the end.

Often they realised that a 'good friend of the family' had, in truth, been the subject's lover in the past and, now they had reunited them, was likely to become one again.

They had subjects nervously waiting for the show to start, after Eamonn had surprised them, 'confessing' they were terrified that Eamonn would introduce on to the programme their mistresses as well as their wives.

Once they discovered on the night immediately before a 'This Is Your Life' that the famous television celebrity who was to be the subject of the following day's show, and whom most of them knew personally – as well as her husband – was having a torrid affair with another friend of theirs.

It happened at the 'read-through'. This was – and no doubt still is – a meeting at which those taking part read and familiarised themselves with the script of the programme. For everything relatives and friends said on the show, based – sometimes very loosely – on the information they had given to researchers, was all written down for them. The location of the 'read-through' had just been moved from a suite at one central London hotel to another. Midway through it one of the researchers went down to the foyer to look for a late-arriving guest and peeped in the bar.

There, in a secluded alcove, was the subject. Not alone but entwined with her lover, while, in the 'read-through' room upstairs, her (less intimate) friends and relatives were, at that very moment, rehearsing all the nice things they were going to say about her on the show next day.

Most worrying of all was that one of them was her husband. Worrying not only because he was in danger of losing a wife but, if he saw her, they would be in danger of losing a programme.

Fortunately, the husband was having something of a torrid affair with a bottle of whisky – which may have explained why his wife had sought the surer hands of her companion downstairs – and so the production team kept its private bar open until both she and her lover had safely left.

There was for them, however, an added piquancy about the touching scenes on the programme next day. Eamonn wondered afterwards what they had all found so amusing.

One of the problems writers had in scripting an authentic 'Life' story was that Eamonn's religion did not recognise divorce and thus neither did Eamonn. In those days if a subject had been involved in one he would not have it mentioned. It was something that just had not happened.

So, at the start of the revival of 'This Is Your Life', divorce was a taboo subject, as were homosexual liaisons, infidelity, illegitimacy, living in sin, and what, in a generic term, Eamonn called 'messy marriages'.

However, as the years went by, a shortage of worthwhile subjects made it a necessity for the longevity of the programme that people who came within those categories were included. So little by little he found euphemisms for them which finally made him feel less uncomfortable when he introduced them.

His poetic phrase for somebody born out of wedlock was, 'The father you never knew left your mother before you were born'.

And, introducing on 'This Is Your Life' a partner with whom the subject was living without the blessing of matrimony, '... and she's here, of course, the woman who shares that life ...'

Even then he was inclined to be influenced by his male chauvinism. When he learned that TV-am presenter Anne Diamond, who had been suggested as a subject, was living with her former producer Mike Hollingsworth, who had left his wife, he snapped, 'Surely you don't imagine I could stand there and say nice things about her! She's a marriage-wrecker!'

And if, on the programme, he could possibly avoid mentioning a situation he considered to be 'unwarm', as he put it, he would do so. If both parents had been married and since separated, but could be persuaded to come together just for the show, he would give no hint when he introduced them of their break-up or subsequent divorce. Instead he would let viewers believe what they were seeing were still happily married parents completing a cosy family scene.

This was the impression given in the 'Lives' of Muhammad Ali, actress Liza Goddard and astrologist Russell Grant, all of whose divorced parents came on together as though they had never been apart.

Despite O'Connor's complaint about Eamonn having failed to mention his eldest daughter, similar things were to happen in two later shows when, again, he decided to disregard the children of earlier marriages. Again both fathers were comedians, Jim Davidson and Freddie Starr.

This time – because of the sensitivity over the O'Connor affair – there was much stronger pressure on him from the team to mention the children, a daughter in Davidson's case, a son in Starr's.

However he was still determined he would not 'if it turns out to be unnecessary' and came up with an opportunistic way the final decision could be made. He would put the onus on the fathers.

He said that just before they stepped in front of the cameras he would tell them there was a mention in the script of the children of their broken marriages. But he would add that he was sorry such a sad note should creep into such a happy occasion, but it did not have to be included unless they insisted.

In neither case was the child mentioned. The omission was at the father's request Eamonn said afterwards. In both cases, however, the fathers later expressed surprise and disappointment the children had been ignored. In neither case did they recall Eamonn ever mentioning the matter to them.

The thing that irritated Eamonn most about the programme was something far less emotional. It was when people such as his dentist or his hairdresser said to him, 'You don't really believe the person you had on last week was surprised, do you? He was so calm he looked as though he was expecting you.'

It was at a programme meeting immediately after his dentist had made such a comment during a conversation about the show that he came out with one of his famous 'curious quotes' which, for his team, became collectors' items. Explaining his reaction to the remark he said, seriously, 'It taught me a lesson, I can tell you. That's the last time I'll open my mouth at the dentist's.'

His hairdresser, too, was the inspiration of a curious quote at a meeting on the morning of a show at which the script was being discussed. Clearly everybody's sanguine attitude at the meeting was irritating him because suddenly he said, 'I called at my barber's on my way here and he said to me, "I can tell you've got a show to do tonight because when you are a bit tense and excited, you get a rash on the back of your neck." Well that's the trouble with this meeting. It's got no effin' rash!'

For years a production assistant carefully kept a note of all his odd sayings to let newcomers know what to expect. Her favourite was a dogmatic statement Eamonn used to bring an end to a discussion about how best to define a tricycle. Thumping the table he cried, with total conviction, 'A tricycle is a bicycle – with three wheels!'

11

To Hollywood in search
of a subject –
and it's no surprise

The frequently asked 'Do you think he knew?' always stung Eamonn to reply, indignantly, 'If I had thought he knew I would not have gone ahead with the programme!' He had always said that during the programme's BBC days. But after Thames revived it he frequently said publicly and even more unequivocally: 'The unbendable rule is that if it is thought the subject even remotely suspects it is about to happen the programme is unhesitatingly and irrevocably scrapped.'

Very forthright. Unfortunately, it was not always true.

Perhaps it was the constant pressure of finding new, rating-pulling subjects week after week, year after year, but as time went on Eamonn found it harder and harder to resist the temptation to bend that rule, or permit it to be bent.

During the three decades the programme was produced up to the time of Eamonn's death, both he and members of the team quite certainly not only suspected some subjects knew – in which case, according to the claim, the shows should have been cancelled – but were totally convinced they knew.

Not surprisingly, therefore, Eamonn himself knew when the programme was about to 'turn the tables' and make him the subject for a second time.

In the show's early BBC days, when Britain bulged with potential subjects, it was not difficult to boast that a programme would be dropped if it was thought the subject suspected. Like the missed bus, there would be another one along in a minute.

Problems really arose when an ITV company started to produce it. Because of the advertising income it attracted they were tempted to keep it running for too long.

In fact, such was the pressure on the production team to come up with new names – and new 'pick-up' ideas – that in 1985 some of them made a plea to Thames to split the annual series of twenty-six consecutive weekly shows into two blocks of thirteen.

That way they would have a three months break in winter as well as summer in which to find more deserving subjects.

But the company turned them down. The dark nights from October to April are rich in ratings for an early evening programme like 'This Is Your Life'.

During his career Eamonn said those words to no fewer than 717 people and although it was frequently described as a once-in-a-lifetime experience suitable subjects were often so scarce that fifteen of those were given that once-in-a-lifetime experience twice in a lifetime.

Besides Eamonn, others were theatrical knights Richard Attenborough, John Mills and Brian Rix, football club manager Sir Matt Busby, theatrical Dames Vera Lynn, Anna Neagle and Eva Turner, film actor Dudley Moore, film actress Diana Dors, singer Petula Clark, band leader Joe Loss, and comedians Arthur Askey, Ted Ray and Norman Wisdom. There would have been more if some, like musical star Tommy Steele, had not disliked the experience so much the first time they made it clear they would not go through it a second time.

Fourteen of the 'two-timers' – as the team called them – had first seen their 'Lives' swim before them at the BBC. But Dudley Moore has been featured twice by the Thames production, the second time in Hollywood when the team was in an even more desperate plight than usual.

Two people have also had that 'unique experience' on both sides of the Atlantic. Hollywood musicals star Alice Faye and singer Frankie Vaughan, who once spent a brief period in Hollywood making a not very memorable film with Marilyn Monroe, have both been the subjects of both the British and American versions.

When plans for new 'Lives' were dying in infancy it was back not to the drawing board but to the dream board. That was a large board covering a wall in the production office divided into twenty-six squares, each marked with a programme date. As a name of a likely subject was proposed, and accepted by Eamonn, it was written in one of the squares.

'Dream board' was a double-edged name for it. Few of the names which originally filled it ever, for a multitude of reasons, went before the cameras and different, usually much less attractive names had to be thought of to replace them.

So tough had the task become at the time of Eamonn's death that at least half-a-dozen 'guests-of-honour' in the last full series he presented were from a 'last resort' list, only to be used when there was nobody more appealing on the horizon.

Some of the names had been on the list, in the lightest of pencil, since the programme's BBC days, and all of them the whole eighteen years Eamonn had presided over it at Thames (like Australian disc jockey Alan Freeman, Jane Rossington of the then expiring soap-opera 'Crossroads' and Fifties singing duo Pearl Carr and Teddy Johnstone).

The shortage caused a particularly bizarre situation for Eamonn when he found himself having to 'honour' a married couple whose names he had turned down year after year because the husband would have himself been presenting the programme on the rival BBC if – according to his version of events – they had timed it better, Cliff Michelmore and his wife Jean Metcalfe. Nor could the programme have been worse timed, because references they had made to him in their recently published joint autobiography had scarcely been complimentary.

Again, less than two months after having to trot out all those nice things about the Michelmores, he then had to pour out the platitudes for David Jacobs, the rival who had tried to revive his other highly successful programme at the BBC, 'What's My Line?'.

So hand-to-mouth had the position so sadly become that when, the year before Eamonn died, the BBC announced a former Fleet Street editor with no radio experience – and who not long before had unsuccessfully sued them for libel – was to become a disc jockey, his name was proposed at the very next programme meeting.

A researcher, however, suggested it might be more sensible if they waited until Derek Jameson had been a disc jockey for a least a month and was a little better known to the public.

But the producer said, 'No, we daren't wait. He might flop and we won't want him then. And we need someone *now*!' The programme was cobbled together in two weeks.

In an attempt to brighten the programme with names that were somewhat more glamorous and better known than Jameson's the team persuaded Thames to let them go to Hollywood to make some shows.

The first was to be on one-time 'golden girl' of Hollywood musicals, Alice Faye. But none of the team really believed for one minute that she did not know they were coming.

Initially Miss Faye was told a British television company wanted to interview her about her career and she agreed. But a strike at Thames delayed the trip and by the time it was rearranged the programme's timing was badly off. By then she was preparing for a three-month, extremely lucrative promotional tour for a cosmetics company and had booked herself into a very expensive health clinic many miles away from Hollywood.

A member of the programme team contacted her American agent who refused even to ask the star to postpone her visit to the clinic. She said that once she had made up her mind to go nothing would make her change it.

The programme even offered to lay on a private jet to fly her from the clinic in Arizona to Hollywood and straight back there. Again the agent refused even to ask her.

So it was decided to pass on the information through a friend and, to strengthen the prospect of getting Miss Faye's co-operation, to upgrade the phoney programme she had been told about. Now it became not merely an interview about her career but a full-scale tribute to her by Thames.

But the friend phoned to say the ploy had not worked. Miss Faye had it firmly fixed in her head that she was going to the clinic and was obstinately sticking to it. She wanted to look good for the tour.

So, in a final attempt, the programme asked an executive of the cosmetics company to intervene. He came back to report that he had managed to persuade her to stay on in Hollywood after all – by telling her, 'in confidence', that what had been planned was a 'surprise tribute by a show that was Britain's kinda "This Is Your Life"'. Another executive told the team afterwards that, in fact, his colleague had not bothered to use the word 'kinda'.

Soon after they set out for Hollywood the team started to wonder why they had even bothered to start on the costly venture in the first place.

Because of the postponement they had been forced to reduce the number of programmes to two. The second was to be on veteran film actress Ann Baxter. But the new popularity she was enjoying in 'Hotel' was very much confined to the television series. After weeks of trying, the team could not find enough friends or relatives to make up a 'This Is Your Life' show. So it had to be called off.

The trip itself was disastrous. Only Eamonn and the producer flew first class, and both got food poisoning.

There was no promised limousine waiting at Los Angeles airport and groggy Eamonn – unrecognised in that part of the world – had to suffer the indignity of standing in a long queue for a taxi.

In addition, one of the team was detained by customs on a false suspicion of attempting to smuggle in drugs.

The programme team's pride was also badly dented at the read-through. Alice Faye's husband, former band leader and singer ('Woodman Spare That Tree') Phil Harris, arrived nearly an hour late and somewhat unsteady. It was carefully explained to him that on the night he would embrace his wife, then sit in the seat next to her until the show was over.

But, as they reached the end of the script, which was packed with the usual pleasantries about his wife, he struggled to his feet and demanded, 'Just a minute, you don't really expect me to sit through all this shit do you?'

One of the principal reasons some production team members were convinced many subjects were in on the secret was spelled out to them by a well-known agent at the party after one of the first Thames productions.

A number of his clients had been subjects in the programme's BBC days and what he said made the soundest sense in a world famed for its rivalry but not for its scruples. He told them, 'None of you can really believe an agent would risk incurring the wrath of a valuable client by permitting him to be submitted to an experience like "This Is Your Life" without first consulting him, or her – even making sure they approved of the people Eamonn was going to "surprise" them with. It would be a tremendous conceit on your part if you did.'

He also claimed that, in addition, nearly all big-name clients demanded to have approval of the guest list, to veto some and ask for others. Without saying who had originated them, of course, either he or the subject's spouse passed these on to the researchers.

This attitude of agents to the programme was confirmed as recently as 1986 when a researcher started work on the 'Life' of a well-known comedian who also aspired to be an actor.

He had a telephone call from the man's venerable old agent who usually left such matters to an assistant and who had obviously forgotten how the game was supposed to be played.

The conversation that followed went exactly like this:–

Agent: 'I'm calling because I'm off to Marbella and you'll need to get started.'

Researcher: 'Yes, please.'

Agent: 'I'll ring him now and get him to ring you.'

Researcher: 'What!'

Agent: 'Well, to give you the list of people he wants. You'll want to know who should be on.'

Researcher: 'Well, er, it's not usual for us to talk to the subject before the programme.'

Agent: 'But he's the best one to speak to.'

Researcher: 'Have you told him already?'

Agent: 'No, no, I'm ringing you because I'm just about to ring him and tell him.'

Researcher: 'You know we're supposed to drop the whole thing if you have told him.'

Agent: 'But *he's* the one who'll know who should be on it.'

Researcher: 'Yes, but what about the surprise?'

Agent: 'Well, he's an *actor*, isn't he?'

The team could hardly blame agents for protecting themselves, against the danger that not telling might cost them valuable clients. After all, the team themselves took similar precautions when Eamonn's 'Life' was made.

That came about because by the time the programme had been on Thames for five years practically every post was bringing letters from viewers challenging them to ring the changes and put Eamonn himself 'in the hot seat'.

They were all from people who either did not know or had

ITA probe joke on Eamonn's TV show

By CLIFFORD DAVIS

THE Independent Television Authority, which controls ITV, is sending for a recording of Sunday night's "Eamonn Andrews Show."

Eamonn told to cut blue jokes

By DOUGLAS MARLBOROUGH

STEPS have been taken to prevent any more blue ... the Eamonn Andrews ... day ITV show ...

ITA may curb Eamonn show

By JACK BELL

THE Independent Television Authority may seek extra safeguards to avoid "errors of taste" in the ABC TV Eamonn Andrews ...

... Show were loaded with ... cuff as out of the rubbish bin. And ... to me about this new programme. ... black sheep of broadcasting and ... golden image.

New clamp-down faces Eamonn

R controls ... on the E... Television ... viewers ... re ...

... in two studios ...

Can the TV star with a family man image keep his public happy on blue jokes?

The Eamonn show is in trouble again

Eamonn's TV guests get a warning

GUESTS on ITV's The Eamonn Andrews Show are to get a fresh warning: KEEP IT CLEAN.

This follows talks ...

Kenneth More—made comments about Mandy Rice-Davies and Elvis Presley's ...

will be warned beforehand not to make remarks which are ... or liable to ...

ABC-TV said last ... "We want the Andrews Show to an audi... spon...

Eamonn – with comedy characters Harold Berens, Gladys Hay and Michael Moore – in his first BBC Radio role as chairman of the cod quiz 'Ignorance Is Bliss'. It was a surprise appointment – he had originally applied for a job as boxing commentator.

Wedding Day, 1951, and beautiful ex-dancer Grace Bourke becomes Mrs Grainne Andrews.

Eamonn has a last-minute word with the author, programme editor Tom Brennand, on the set before the very first transmission of 'The Eamonn Andrews Show' in 1964.

Eamonn's handling of British television's first chat-show led to much unkind Press reaction, including this comment by caricaturist Gerald Scarfe.

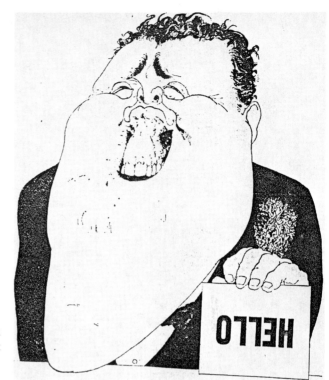

Bob Hope and Bing Crosby's second double-act appearance as guests of Eamonn's chat-show. On the first, Bing wore his toupee, not a cap, and that later caused Eamonn some confusion.

In 1973 the author, Tom Brennand (centre) – then programme-consultant and writer of 'This Is Your Life' – realised an old school-pal, missionary priest Father Francis O'Leary, who founded the world-wide hospice organisation Jospice International, would make an ideal subject. So he lured him to a surprise confrontation with Eamonn.

And Niamh makes three. Eamonn and Grainne with Emma and Fergal shortly after they had adopted eighteen-week-old Niamh to complete the family.

Although heart disease was sapping his strength, Eamonn carried on working until his death, two months after this picture was taken.

forgotten Eamonn was, in fact, the subject of the first ever BBC 'This Is Your Life'.

The production team certainly did not want to take the risk that he would hate it if it happened to him again, so at the start of the next series the then producer asked him straight out how he would feel if somebody else confronted *him* with the book.

Eamonn replied that he would not mind as long it was the very last programme of the series so it would not be a case of him being 'surprised' one week himself then surprising somebody else the following week.

It was, therefore, hardly a shock for him when, at the very end of that series, David Nixon, an old friend from the panel of 'What's My Line?', popped up with the 'This Is Your Life' book when he arrived ostensibly to make a 'guest' appearance on the magician's own show.

The programme had not been back on television a full year when members of the production team first learned of a subject, comedian Bob Hope, who was already in on the secret.

And the ironic thing was that the team had, at one stage, been thrown into a panic because they thought he was about to discover all their plans by sheer accident.

Hope was about to fly to London for a charity concert when they decided to make him the subject of an hour-long 'This Is Your Life' special and asked his Hollywood office for permission to go ahead. Shortly afterwards permission was granted. And, though, of course, they did not know it at the time, the person who gave them that permission was Bob Hope himself.

Immediately the approach had been made, his private secretary of many years, Marjorie Hughes, had told him all about their plans – for similar reasons as those the agent had outlined at the very start of the programme's revival at Thames.

Totally unaware that the whole operation had now become a charade, the programme team arranged to fly Hope's wife, Dolores, and their four grown-up children to London from their home in California, after he had left himself, to be his first 'surprise', and started inviting the line up of celebrities Hope's aides were kind enough to supply with a little help from the man himself.

Meantime, more farce was to follow. When the family arrived in London Hope's daughter, Linda, visited a West End hairstylist's salon where, by chance, she met a friend from home, Frank Sinatra's daughter, Tina.

Tina was about to be photographed at the salon for a newspaper and when she introduced Hope's daughter to the photographer he asked her to be in the picture, too.

Linda agreed and the newspaper got its 'exclusive' picture of the glamorous daughters of two of the world's most famous entertainers meeting by accident in London. Shortly afterwards, however, Linda remembered that the people who had gone to the trouble and expense of flying the family to London had solemnly asked them to remain incognito until the programme was over. Having her photograph published in a mass circulating daily was hardly the best way of abiding by that request. She told her mother about the picture and mum passed the tidings to the programme.

Understandably, the team were convinced that if Hope saw a picture of his daughter in London the surprise of the whole show would be 'blown'. So, unaware he already knew not only that the whole family was there but exactly who else they had also lined up to 'surprise' him with, they took the newspaper into their confidence and asked them not to publish it until the programme was 'in the can'.

As they feared, their approach at first only served to heighten the newspaper's interest in the photograph. But eventually they took the view that by publishing it they would be 'spoiling the pleasure' of millions of viewers and, to the team's profound relief, decided to withhold it.

So Hope duly headed for the Thames studios pretending to believe the story he had been told that he was going there to be interviewed for their London magazine programme.

Then, when Eamonn pounced on him in the foyer, he looked suitably startled. And he continued to feign near-swooning amazement and disbelief as he was greeted by his family and a seemingly endless flow of the famous, including Earl Mountbatten of Burma, with whom he had been involved in charity work, Walter Annenberg, then US ambassador to Britain, evangelist Billy Graham, golfer Arnold Palmer, his co-stars in his 'Road' films, Bing Crosby and Dorothy Lamour, and other Hollywood stars, among them John Wayne, Gregory Peck, Jack Benny, Sammy Davis Junior, and Rosemary Clooney.

After it was all over, the relieved production team told Hope how he had come so near to having the whole surprise spoiled by seeing Linda's photograph in a British newspaper. He seemed to find that rather amusing. Shortly afterwards – when he told a biographer that he had 'been with Eamonn's plans every step of the way' – they knew why.

Having worked with Hope before and being aware of his absolute insistence on having total control of all of his public appearances, Eamonn must have been pretty sure he would have been in on the secret even before he admitted that had been the case.

Half way through the preparations for the 'This Is Your Life' of actress Joan Collins he had similar very strong suspicions she, too, was completely in step with everything that was being planned.

Appropriately the 'Life' of the star of the soap-opera 'Dynasty' became one of the greatest sagas ever encountered by 'This Is Your Life', full of mystery and deceit and owing as much to fiction as it did to fact.

Sensibly Eamonn did what he usually did with all television sagas – tried to ignore it.

However, not only did the production team have no doubts Miss Collins knew all along, they also suspected – again as the agent had warned of stars of her calibre – she was manipulating the whole show without them being able to do anything about it.

Until they had convinced Eamonn, who, of course, watched very little television, that 'Dynasty', in which she had then been starring for a year, really had made Joan Collins an actress of international stature, he could not be persuaded to feature her on the programme. He could not abide the thought of what he called her 'messy marriages' to actors Maxwell Reed and Anthony Newley.

A big worry the team had about Miss Collins was that they had been hearing reports that her then current ten-year marriage to film producer Ron Kass was also getting pretty messy.

They decided to go ahead in the hope that the almost inevitable split would not happen before the day of the show. And, so as not to gamble a further second on the chance the marriage would crumble completely between the recording and the actual transmission, they decided it would have to be a live programme – which, conveniently, would also fill a gap that had suddenly occurred in their schedule.

At the time, her father, Joe Collins, who was a veteran theatrical agent, was about to reach his eightieth birthday, an occasion they reckoned they could use to lure Miss Collins back to London. Mr Collins, not unnaturally, agreed to give his complete co-operation.

The first thought was that they should pay him to throw a huge birthday party to which she would be invited, and where Eamonn would make 'the pick-up'.

But they realised, that, despite such an important milestone in her father's life, they would need extra insurance to be confident she would make the journey from Hollywood to London in November.

One way was to turn the air trip into an ego trip. They decided to tell her television cameras would also be at the party to publicise her starring role in 'Dynasty'. Afterwards they wondered why they had bothered to go to so much trouble. But at that time they were not aware she already knew what was being planned. However, all the signs were there. It was a long shot that an actress so much in demand as her would be prepared to take practically a week out of her schedule to attend a birthday party six thousand miles away. But the message was that she would.

And they could hardly believe how well things were going when husband Kass agreed to make a secret flight to London with their nine-year-old daughter, Katy, to be the soap star's first 'surprise' on the show.

Then came a setback. They were told Miss Collins was not prepared to leave the States until the very last moment – on the day of the show, in fact. It meant she would not arrive at Heathrow in time to put in an appearance at the phoney party, and then be driven to the studio in time for the show's seven o'clock start.

The only way was to take her straight from the airport to the studio and for Eamonn to 'confront' her at the studio door.

So they invented a story that, again to mark her father's eightieth birthday, Thames Television wanted to record an interview about the family's long history in showbusiness and would like his famous daughter to be at his side.

They thought they were pushing their luck by apparently putting such demands on the time of such a temperamental lady, but it was a risk they had to take if they were to get the programme they so badly needed to fill a worrying hole in their schedule.

They could scarcely believe their luck had held when the message came back that she would do it.

Or was it really their luck, they now began to wonder.

Well, that was something they were not going to think too much about. The important thing was they were all set to go.

But, as the day approached more strange and unnerving things began to happen.

Out of the blue, her agent informed them Miss Collins was bringing Katy with her on the trip. So, where was husband Kass?

Ah, he would now be secretly flying to London alone the day before. But it turned out to be such a well-kept secret that apparently even Kass himself was not in on it. Because when they sent a programme representative to meet the flight, he was not on it.

Twenty-four hours to the show and no husband.

Then came another message. Collins, Kass and Katy would all be travelling together on the day of the show – 'as a family'.

Odd in the circumstances. But a relief just the same.

Not for long though. A few hours later an agitated Thames Television press office told the production team they had just had a call from a British newspaperman in New York who had informed them he knew Joan Collins was flying to London with her husband and daughter to appear on 'This Is Your Life'.

What was more important, the reporter had said Miss Collins knew she was to be the subject of the programme. She was fully aware the birthday party and the supposed television interview were just ruses to get her over so that Eamonn could 'surprise' her.

The same reporter had written a story weeks earlier claiming Miss Collins and Kass had separated. He told the press office he knew she had temporarily got together with him simply to give the impression they were still a united family, so the programme would go ahead and she would benefit from the publicity.

So, it seemed, that was the end of that. The secret had been blown. There could be no show now.

But they soon found an argument for not tossing away all that work. They told themselves they only had the journalist's word for it that Miss Collins knew. After all, they had not heard it from her own lacquered lips.

There were also one or two other persuasive arguments for not abandoning the show.

Such as the fact that the programme had already spent many thousands of pounds filming 'tributes' in various parts of America from some very big star names – among them John Forsythe and Linda Evans, from 'Dynasty', Gregory Peck and Robert Wagner, with whom she had made films, and her novelist sister, Jackie.

Some cynical people might have thought it strange that daughter Jackie could not find the time to fly from California for her old dad's birthday, while her frantically busy sister – who just happened to be the intended subject of 'This Is Your Life' – somehow could. But that was no concern of the production team.

Another pretty convincing argument was that they had already flown in film actors David McCallum and Farley Granger from New York, and from Paris, where they were in boarding school, her two children from her marriage to Anthony Newley. Also already assembled were her brother Bill, half-sister, Natasha, and, of course, father, Joe.

To slap on more dollops of sentiment they had invited seven nurses who helped look after daughter Katy while she was in a coma after being injured in a road accident; singer Roger Whittaker, who flew Miss Collins in his private plane from Paris to Katy's hospital bedside in London; and a couple with their young daughter, who had, happily, come out of a coma after a similar road accident, and who had sent Miss Collins messages of encouragement while Katy was in danger.

And, in case the audience was not already awash with tears by then, they had also flown from Bombay a young, fatherless Indian girl who had been rescued from poverty by a charity Miss Collins supported.

Now who was going to scrap all that expensive film and tell all those guests to go home programme-less just because some reporter three thousand miles away in New York said the subject knew all about them and not one 'surprise' would be unexpected? Certainly not the production team.

So they pushed on with the next part of the programme-schedule, the read-through.

During it the director automatically asked Miss Collins's father, the stock question, 'How do you think Joan will react when Eamonn steps out to surprise her?'

The moment the question was out, the assembled team realised that, with all the alarm bells that had already been ringing, this was one time it should not have been asked.

Too late. As they sat mesmorised, they heard old Joe say with a frankness that astounded them 'Don't worry, she'll act it out beautifully.'

The only sound was the sharp intake of breath as the members of the production team shot anxious glances at each other.

Here was the subject's father saying, as though it was something that was taken for granted, that the degree of surprise his daughter would convey when Eamonn swooped on her with the big red book would simply be a test of her acting ability. Not only that, he was inferring that such a reaction was not unexceptional – and it had to be remembered that he was a theatrical agent of long standing some of whose clients had been subjects of the programme in the past.

Perhaps the team should not have been so taken aback as they had been.

After all – it was something all of them believed to be the case, anyway. It was just that nobody had dared say it out loud before.

Fortunately, none of the other guests taking their seats seemed to have heard what Joe Collins had said. So the team pretended they had not heard either.

There were more heart-stopping moments on the morning of the show when they saw a national newspaper's front page headline, 'Joan Collins In TV Riddle'. But fortunately the reporter had gone along with the press office's pleas 'not to spoil it for viewers', because his story said only that Miss Collins and her estranged husband had left Los Angeles together for 'a mystery TV appearance' in London. However, significantly he had added the words, 'They are only going through a charade for reasons that will become evident.'

So Miss Collins duly arrived and, without a further hitch, became the 590th subject of the 'This Is Your Life' programme on British television.

Nothing of father Joe's candid comment about her daughter's reaction had been mentioned to Eamonn. He knew only of the mysterious changes that kept occurring in her plans, the equally mysterious amount of co-operation she was giving Thames Television and the newspaperman's claims. His strict instruction was that whenever the team suspected the subject knew, he was to be kept in total ignorance of it.

Then he could say, hand on heart, that *he* did not know for certain that the subject was in on the secret.

When he stepped out to confront Miss Collins as she was ushered through the studio doors, she did, as forecast by father, act out her surprise very convincingly.

The show ended with her and Kass side by side, the very picture of a happily married couple. Two months later their separation was announced officially.

Meantime, two newspapers had named her as their actress of the year. Not for her role in 'Dynasty' but for looking surprised and happily married on 'This Is Your Life'.

That, however, was something with which I had to disagree.

I had encountered her twice before in my career. The first was four years earlier when she was the guest on Thames Television's doomed attempt to revive Eamonn's Sixties chat show. When I met her the second time, on a programme at Tyne Tees Television, I reminded her of this.

It was a mistake.

To my surprise, she rounded on me and snarled, 'You didn't have anything to do with that did you! I can't stand that idiot Eamonn Andrews!'

So, in the estimation of many, her best acting performance was not pretending to be surprised to see Eamonn, but pretending to be *pleased* to see him.

12

Lord Louis, Prince Charles – and Her Majesty

Joe Collins's candid remark, reassuring though it was meant to be, that when Eamonn confronted her with the big red book his Dynasty daughter would act out a pretence at being surprised, was far from the only shock the production team got at a read-through.

For the people who put the programme together, the read-through really was the moment of truth (the more cynical among them said it was one of the few moments of truth in the whole proceedings, and that included the programme itself). It was also the moment researchers, who until then had been talking to the guests of the show as a set of individuals, found out how they would behave as a mob.

In the preceding weeks, amid tearful talk of reunions with long-lost brothers and sisters, the guests had gratefully accepted the offers of free trips to London from various parts of the world.

Not forgetting a minimum of three days first class hotel accommodation in the capital, recompense for any loss of earnings and any expense incurred, and free food and drink – of which large quantities tended to be consumed.

Finally came the night of the read-through when they were all brought together for the first time, often still tired from the journey and over-emotional from the amount of free booze with which they had eased the hours of travel.

It was the moment the veils dropped, or could no longer be held up; now they revealed what they really felt about each other and the production team discovered which factions of the family hated which.

It was an event from which Eamonn stayed away. And sensibly so. It was part of the policy of keeping the less palatable truth away from his innocent ears. If he had been privy to some of the things the rest of the team heard at those gatherings he would have found it extremely difficult, as pragmatic as he was, to have looked many of those subjects straight in the eye on the programme itself and say all those nice things about them.

For there were many not-so-nice things the team learned when it brought back together a splintered family. And the first was why it became splintered in the first place.

The Adamsons, the three sisters and two brothers of Peter Adamson, who for more than twenty years was the extremely popular Len Fairclough in the top soap opera 'Coronation Street', were a splintered family.

Their reunion for 'This Is Your Life' had an extra piquancy. They all totally disliked the man they had come together to 'honour'.

In fact one brother, Clifford, was forthright enough to admit, after all the pretence had been made on the programme, that they only agreed to go ahead because they realised it was their chance to see again another brother who was in failing health. He had lived in Canada for nearly forty years and they knew 'This Is Your Life' would fly him home for the show, something he could not afford to do himself.

The charade that they were one big, happy family, delighted that Eamonn had brought them all back together again, just about lasted the programme. But it did not last the night. When the show was over Peter Adamson totally ignored a family party which his brothers and sisters had arranged at the hotel at which they were staying and made no further attempt to communicate with them.

During their original inquiries researchers learned that in past years Adamson's mother, an amiable eccentric who died before the programme was made, was in the habit of handing out visiting cards which bore the legend below her name, 'Mother of Len Fairclough'. It was considered unwise at the time to take her into their confidence about the plan for the programme, as would have been necessary, in case she had the bizarre idea of advertising that, too. So, as she was already rather elderly, they simply decided to shelve it until she had died.

It was the team's normal reaction to such problems which seemed likely to be solved by a not-too-distant bereavement.

Shocks and surprises were not the only diversions a read-through had in store. When they were asked to read aloud that part of the script they were required to repeat on the programme, heated arguments regularly broke out among relatives as they contradicted the researchers, the writers, and themselves, about when and where the subject *really* did what, and with whom.

But, as the writers naturally believed what they had written was a vast improvement on the guests' own ideas of what the truth of the matter was, they were almost always persuaded to stick to what was in the script.

They were never actually told that unless they did they would no longer be required to contribute to the programme and their impending few moments of fame, to which, despite all exhortations for secrecy, they had doubtless alerted just about everybody they knew, would be snatched from them.

But it was always impressed on them that the programme was so crammed with good things that something, or somebody, would almost certainly have to be cut out before the show went on the air.

That usually resulted in everybody being totally attentive at the full-scale programme rehearsals next day, with not another complaint about the script. Rather, by then, they had usually become very well versed in the words which the writers had put into their mouths.

Despite the pandemonium they frequently caused, the family disagreements were not discouraged. Occasionally they produced anecdotes which the researchers had not discovered, and which, if they were not suitable for the show, sometimes at least broke up the boredom.

The read-through of the programme on former star of the television series 'The Avengers', Patrick McNee, led to a bizarre exchange between his daughter and her mother, McNee's former wife. The programme was unique because it was the first 'This Is Your Life', on which a subject's divorced partner was not only acknowledged but actually appeared. But that exchange nearly prevented it happening.

When the programme was made McNee had lived for years in America with his daughter, Jenny, on whom he doted.

The wife, Barbara, from whom he had been divorced for many more years than that, had also gone to America to pursue her own career as an actress and, the years having healed the wounds, she and McNee were back on amicable terms.

So much so that the daughter convinced the production team that not only would it *not* be embarrassing for her mother to appear on the show but that her father would welcome it and, in fact, be disappointed if she were omitted.

However, during the read-through, Jenny, now very much the self-confident Californian young lady who had by then spent much more time with McNee than her mother, kept interrupting to mention events in her father's life, most of them irrelevant, that had not been included in the script.

Many of these references were obviously not within her mother's knowledge and she, like the rest of those in the crowded room, was clearly becoming impatient at her daughter's continual interjections.

Eventually she turned to her and said, 'You seem to know much more about your father than I do.'

To which her daughter replied, 'Yes, and here's something else you don't know about Daddy. You were his first fuck!'

The mother was so stunned by the indelicacy of the remark, for some minutes it seemed she was about to head straight back to the airport.

Like Mr and Mrs McNee, Muhammad Ali's parents had been divorced many years before the 'This Is Your Life' they appeared on, but the programme united them temporarily and he didn't blink an eye when they were brought on together and sat side by side, in hand-holding closeness, a touching picture of devoted, Deep-South, Darby and Joan togetherness.

And no wonder. Very little, if indeed anything, on Ali's 'This Is Your Life' was as presented to the viewers.

For one thing Ali knew, of course, and Eamonn knew he knew. At that time he was at the top of the boxing business and one of the 'hottest properties' in the world. He did not do anything or go anywhere, let alone suddenly be persuaded to take off from Kentucky for England in mid-winter, without knowing *precisely* why. He was far too astute, and too much in control, to be misled by the kind of ruse 'This Is Your Life' got away with on its home territory.

However, the decision that he should be the subject of a double-length 'special' to be transmitted at Christmas to challenge the BBC's traditional dominance of the viewing at that time of the year had been made by somebody of considerable influence in the Thames Television hierarchy.

Eamonn, for all his talk of ultimately making his own programme decisions, was far too streetwise ever to argue at that level, even if he had been disposed to do so.

As long as he seemed likely to get what he considered to be a good show out of it in the end, he was not really concerned that many of the major moves in setting it up had been taken out of the hands of his colleagues on the production team.

Later they were to read newspaper reports from America that for agreeing to be the subject of the British 'This Is Your Life' Ali was paid more than $50,000 and that he gave a list of twelve people he wanted to appear on the programme to his representative with the International Management Group in New York. The reports were never denied.

But the first real evidence the team had that Ali knew was when the former policeman who had first encouraged him to take up boxing told them he had bumped into Ali the week before in his home town of Louisville and unthinkingly had said how much he was looking forward to appearing on his show in London, to which Ali had merely shrugged. Then other guests from Kentucky revealed that on the day before Ali left there the Louisville Daily News had published a story announcing that he was off to London to be the subject of 'This Is Your Life'.

Another subject members of the production team were told was in on the secret was pop-singer-turned-charity-campaigner Bob Geldof. But he would not have been a subject at all if Eamonn had stuck by his original objection to the idea.

The reason he disliked Geldof was that a few years earlier he had had a fierce clash with him on the chat show he was trying to revive and had not forgiven him.

During the programme Geldof, himself a Dubliner, made an

attack on the Catholic priests – and what he called their sadistic streak – who had taught him.

Eamonn, who, of course, had also been taught by a religious order in Dublin, and had also often been subjected to severe beatings, nevertheless felt it his duty to defend them. He made it clear he regarded Geldof's onslaught a near sacrilegious attack on the Faith of which he was a defender.

However, by the time Geldof's name came up at a 'This Is Your Life' meeting his work in organising Band Aid to raise money to feed the starving of Ethiopia and the Sudan had made him one of the most admired men living. Eamonn had little choice but to agree to confront him with the book.

Geldof was in Ethiopia at the time and his girlfriend, later his wife, Paula Yates, agreed to co-operate for the sake of the extra publicity the programme would give to Band Aid.

Geldof was to return to London on the day before the programme was to be made. But with a week to go the team heard from journalists who were accompanying him that he had announced he was going to continue his tour into the Sudan. He would not now be returning until after the programme day.

So, anxiously, they asked the journalists to try to persuade him to return to his original plans.

And, despite the fact that he was renowned for his stubbornness, they eventually did. But, one of them confessed, they managed it during a night's drinking session at their hotel in Addis Ababa by the simple device of telling him that if he returned as planned he would get even more publicity for his Band Aid appeal – on 'This Is Your Life'.

So Geldof returned to his original schedule and the production team carried on with the programme as though they did not know he even had the faintest suspicion of what was about to happen. They saw no sense in telling Eamonn how the journalist had got him to change his mind. In any event when Geldof's name had first come up he had said, 'You don't believe that girl he lives with will keep the secret do you?'

Members of the team did not, of course convey any of this to the friends of Geldof who were appearing in the show. But then they did not believe it was going to come as a surprise to him either.

One of them, a schooldays friend who had since become a

businessman in Dublin, had already said he would know if Geldof was in on the secret the moment he saw Eamonn confront him.

'If he doesn't know what's about to happen he'll be unshaven and wearing scruffy-looking clothes,' the friend said.

When Eamonn presented him with the book Geldof was clean shaven and wearing a smart leather jacket and collar and tie.

Nobody, neither Eamonn, the production team, nor, one imagines, most of the viewers, really believed that Earl Mountbatten of Burma did not know about the plans for his 'This Is Your Life'.

Only a very foolish optimist would be convinced it was possible to spend months probing into the past of somebody of such exalted rank, and even manipulate some of his movements, without him getting a whiff of it.

But Eamonn would have found it impossible anyway to resist a cast which, apart from Lord Mountbatten's family and former Naval colleagues, was to include Dame Vera Lynn, the Hollywood child star of his youth, Jackie Coogan, Lord Bernard Miles, Sir John Mills and his daughter Juliet Mills, Bob Hope, Danny Kaye, and Douglas Fairbanks Junior, whose parents, Douglas Fairbanks and Mary Pickford, lent their Hollywood home 'Pickfair' to Lord and Lady Mountbatten for their honeymoon.

But the real cachet for Eamonn was that at last he was about to have Prince Charles on one of his programmes. Lord Louis was Prince Charles's favourite uncle and he had agreed to make a contribution to his 'Life'.

Eamonn had already been introduced to the Queen, of course, and later he was to meet Prince Andrew when he helped to 'snare' royal photographer Norman Parkinson for the programme.

The Queen Mother, too, once helped the programme team get their man. The subject that time was Sir Fitzroy Maclean, one of the founders of the Special Air Service who helped organise Marshall Tito's wartime guerrillas in German-occupied Yugoslavia.

When the programme was being planned Sir Fitzroy no longer very often left his home near Loch Fyne, in Argyllshire, Scotland, and the worry was how to lure him to London. When the Queen Mother heard this from a member of the Maclean clan she solved the programme's problem by inviting him to a luncheon at Clarence House, and he, of course, accepted immediately.

Eamonn's reaction to this news was that the programme should push its luck even further and instructed the team to invite the Queen Mother to appear on Sir Fitzroy's 'Life' herself. When she declined to appear either in person or on film he even made a last ditch effort by telling them to get a request to her to write at least a few words of tribute to the war hero for Eamonn to read on the programme. But back came the reply from a Clarence House spokesman, in his words rather than hers, one suspects, 'The Queen Mother would be happy to pay tribute to an ordinary person but not one of stature'.

That may have been a big disappointment for Eamonn, but the news that Prince Charles *was* going to appear on a programme had him really excited. To add the next King of England to the list of Royals with whom he had already been 'associated' ... the Paddy from beyond the pale had come a long way from Synge Street.

Buckingham Palace made it clear from the start that protocol would prevent Prince Charles from appearing in person. But he was happy to film a message – and maybe even include a reference to Eamonn in it.

So arrangements were made for a camera crew to go to the Palace where Prince Charles, who had not yet married, was still living, to film him there.

Because of the greater than normal interest he was taking in these plans, the production team realised Eamonn was itching to break his career-long rule not to get involved in any of the physicals of programme preparation and accompany the team members who were going to meet Prince Charles and set up his contribution.

He managed to resist going that far but, nevertheless, he could not wait to hear the outcome (and, without saying so, if Prince Charles had given him a personal mention). So on the day fixed for the filming he just happened to call in at the production office.

But, to his surprise, the team members who were supposed to be at the Palace were still there. He wanted to know why.

A researcher explained that the Prince's Press Officer had telephoned earlier that morning and said, 'The young man raised it with his mother for the first time at dinner last night.'

But what about the film?

The researcher said Prince Charles would not be making it, after all.

'Why not?' Eamonn demanded to know.

'Because,' the researcher told him, 'in the words of the Press Officer, his mother won't let him!'

13

A home in Ireland
and some shocks
in New York

'This Is Your Life' was starting only the second year of its successful Thames revival when Grainne's decision to return to Dublin became final. By then Emma had reached the age when she was due to start at primary school and Fergal was old enough for the infants' school.

It was her desire that the children should be 'brought up Irish' that clinched it, Eamonn told me at the time. Emma had been attending a West London infants' school for three years and, said Eamonn, 'She is starting to talk like the local kids. Grainne can't abide it.'

Colleagues and executives at Thames Television and in London business circles, and old friends at the BBC, were all surprised when Eamonn let it be known in the summer of 1970 that he was selling his beautiful Thames-side house and setting up home in Ireland, which he had left twenty years before. They wondered if it was a decision he would live to regret.

For a man in sight of his fiftieth birthday the prospect of commuting by air between Dublin and London every week – especially throughout the winter months – for the rest of his foreseeable working life was a daunting one. So, too, was the prospect of spending only half of his life with his family in Ireland and the rest of it living on his own in London.

But it was for the sake of the family that he decided that was the way it must be.

Ironically, the decision was made only seven years after he had written in his autobiography the line in which he voiced the view that continual separation of husband and wife was the main reason for the high mortality rate among show business marriages.

There seemed little danger that the separations caused by the move to Ireland would threaten his marriage, however. But there was no question that he would have to continue to work as hard as ever once he had settled there. The costs of the new house, designed as a 'space-age mansion', he and Grainne were having built near the sea at Portmarnock, soon started to mount alarmingly.

It had begun as a bungalow on the site of a disused quarry, reached by a rough, uphill drive, which Eamonn told me he had managed to get cheap from an Aer Lingus pilot who had gone bust building it.

That was to be the only thing remotely cheap about the venture.

Eamonn and Grainne engaged one of Ireland's leading architects who came up with a plan to build the new house around the existing bungalow, so they could live there while it was taking shape.

That meant, however, that it was too dangerous for the rock on the quarry site to be removed by explosives and it had to be chipped away much more expensively.

Then there was the question of the swimming pool already built near to the quarry face. It looked fine on a sunny summer's day with the children splashing about in it, but for the rest of the time it was a sombre looking place. So it was extended further into the quarry to make it appear to be a natural part of it, and to enhance this effect a waterfall was created to tumble into it from the rocks above.

Then the bungalow's normal size living room grew to spectacular dimensions becoming a room with a ceiling twenty foot high overlooked by a gallery and a dining-room.

A fireplace ran the whole length of one side of the room and another wall consisted almost completely of a high, curved window which opened on to the waterfall-splashed pool and gave access to terraces and patios. Above a recessed bar was Eamonn's study with a window from which he could look down into the living room. There were also five bedrooms and maid's quarters.

All of this Grainne turned into 'a symphony in white', with white walls and ceilings, and long-haired white carpets or white tiles.

With all the commuting, life had become so frantic for Eamonn that sometimes he had to meet the architect at London's Heathrow airport and discuss progress and problems during the flight to Dublin.

In all, it took four years to complete and one of the first journalists shown around it declared it to be 'a cross between a castle and a cathedral'.

When the family moved back to Ireland, Eamonn, in addition to 'This Is Your Life' on Wednesday nights, was also fronting Thames Television's four-nights-a-week London news-magazine programme, 'Today'.

From then on, and until he died in 1987, it meant he had to maintain a punishing itinerary.

He would leave his home early each Monday morning and drive to Dublin airport for a ten o'clock flight to London. At Heathrow a car would be waiting to take him to his London flat, just a mile from his former home in Chiswick, where he would have meetings with his secretary and the editor of 'Today' and collect the latest draft of the script of that week's 'This Is Your Life'.

In the early afternoon he would be driven to the studio where he would study the notes on that night's show, and the script, in his dressing room. Then it was into the studio for a 'dry run', then back to his dressing room to be made-up before returning to the studio at 5.55 for the show's six o'clock start.

Immediately 'Today' was over he would go straight back to his dressing room, removing his tie as he went, and gratefully pull off his sweat-soaked jacket and shirt, and towel his perspiring face.

His critics made much mention of the amount Eamonn sweated throughout his programmes, as though it was an indication of how much he was inwardly panicking. It was a fact that nervousness made him sweat more than most and during moments in shows when the cameras were briefly off him a waiting make-up girl would swiftly step forward and sponge his glistening brow. But it was also true that those critics overlooked the fact that throughout 'This Is Your Life', at least, Eamonn was not sitting but standing under those desert-hot television lights with his six-feet-one-inch height bringing his head close to them and making them feel even hotter.

Sometimes, however, there were other reasons than the lights why he perspired heavily. The most common reason was when unpredictable people were guests on a show, especially comedians like Tommy Cooper, Frankie Howerd and Spike Milligan, who refused to stick to a script.

It *was* fairly predictable, however, that performers like those would cause some sort of mayhem. But some moments that made Eamonn sweat could never be anticipated.

Because of actor Trevor Howard's reputation as an imbiber, it was expected that when he arrived to take part in the 'Life' of octogenarian actress Joyce Carey he would have fortified himself with a drink or two. What was not anticipated was that he would have had so much that the production team would be divided as to whether or not he should be allowed to go on at all.

Eventually they decided to avoid the embarrassment that shipping him off home would cause and take the risk of letting him go on to say a few words of tribute to the actress who had appeared with him many years before in the film 'Brief Encounter'.

But what viewers watching did not realise – although Eamonn did, to his discomfort – was that when Howard appeared to throw his arms around Miss Carey's neck in affectionate greeting he was really throwing his arms around her to keep himself from falling flat on his face, because he had drunkenly lost his balance as he staggered on.

And what viewers did not realise, either, was that when, afterwards, Miss Carey sat apparently nervously fiddling with an earring under her elegantly coiffured hair, she was really desperately trying, but failing, to replace the hearing-aid Howard had knocked out as he clung to her. So for the rest of the programme she had to rely on her lip-reading skills to fathom out who Eamonn was introducing and, when they came on, what on earth they were talking about.

Another guest who caused Eamonn to sweat more than usual was comedy actor Alfie Bass when he came on the 'Life' of the actor with whom he had sprung to fame in the television series 'The Army Game', Bill Fraser. As they stood side by side at the rehearsal Eamonn winced in pain as Bass playfully stole an arm around his back, took hold of a chunk of the flesh of his backside and gripped it hard.

So to avoid a repetition Eamonn made a point of standing almost-face-to-face with Bass when he came on the show itself, practically keeping his back to the camera. But it did not work.

Because instead of his backside Bass grabbed hold of his testicles and kept squeezing until he had finished playing his tribute to his old friend.

Although he had never before been known to cry during even the weepiest of 'This Is Your Life' programmes, Eamonn had tears in his eyes, as well as sweat on his brow, that night.

The moment he discarded his perspiration-soaked clothing after any programme Eamonn immediately phoned Grainne, a framed photograph of whom stood alongside miniatures of all their three children on his dressing table, even after 'Today' which, being a London-only show, she was not able to see.

When he called about a programme she was able to receive in Ireland, such as 'This Is Your Life' or 'What's My Line?', she told him precisely what she thought of his performance, his appearance and the programme itself and he paid a great deal of attention to what she said. He very much valued her judgement which sometimes included her opinion of the programme sets and furniture.

After his call, Eamonn would go to the hospitality room for drinks with the programme guests and production team and then a car would take him back to his flat. Sometimes he would eat supper there alone or sometimes invite a colleague to join him for a plate of his own Irish Stew, which people who really knew about the dish considered to be quite delicious.

Bill Grundy, Eamonn's stand-in, took the 'Today' chair on Wednesdays when he was presenting 'This Is Your Life', and on Tuesday evenings Eamonn would discuss the following day's 'Life' programme with the producer, usually by telephone.

On Wednesday morning he would be driven to the 'This Is Your Life' studio for a nine o'clock meeting – sometimes even earlier if the 'pick-up' was to be made outside London – to discuss the script, and the final confrontation plan. Then he would go into the studio for two rehearsals of the programme with all the guests, except of course, the 'guest-of-honour'.

Following that he would be driven to the chosen location for the 'pick-up', a procedure which was often physically demanding and always emotionally draining.

After the show itself, which, depending on at what time of day it was best to 'surprise' the subject, was frequently recorded very late in the evening, he would watch a play-back of it at a reception for everybody involved and, finally, be driven back to his empty flat at Chiswick.

Next morning he would attend a meeting to discuss the following week's 'This Is Your Life' and listen to progress reports on any that were being planned for the weeks ahead. Then he was off to the 'Today' studio for the Thursday night show, usually his last of the week, after which he was off to Heathrow for a late night flight back to Dublin.

To complicate matters further, for technical reasons or because of the availability of 'subjects', 'This Is Your Life' 'pick-ups' or whole programmes were occasionally recorded in America or on the Continent and once in the Kenyan bush, which added many thousand more flying miles to that exhausting itinerary.

While flying back home from a programme in Scotland – on Scots Olympic sprinter Allan Wells – he had the alarming experience of his plane being struck by lightning, not once but twice.

However, the object of a lot of this travelling was to permit him to spend at least most weekends, from Friday night to Monday morning, at his Dublin home. But even that time was filled with business meetings about his companies which together comprised the biggest entertainments conglomorate in Ireland.

To keep fit he jogged every morning – when he was at home – around his three-and-a-half acres and struggled through the occasional game of golf off a seldom played-to 18 handicap. He also went riding until he was in his mid-fifties when he was thrown from his horse and bruised more than his pride.

It was in the kitchen he got most pleasure and he would make a great fuss if a cooking receptacle had been used in his absence and put away in the wrong place. He most enjoyed baking bread, probably because it reminded him of how in his childhood he used to watch his mother make circular loaves of soda bread using the frying pan as a baking-tin in the tiny kitchen of their Dublin council house and wait until she handed him the first hot, floury slice with the butter still melting into it.

In the somewhat larger kitchen of the Portmarnock mansion, never failing to don an apron, he also cooked the family's Sunday breakfast of pancakes and syrup. Frequently he cooked Sunday lunch, too, carefully rechecking everything in a recipe book although he had prepared the same meal hundreds of times before. And he always cooked Christmas lunch, after first pinning to his apron a list of everything he had to do.

When he returned to London after the weekend, Grainne occasionally accompanied him to visit the shops. But often they were working, not buying, trips. She had never lost the skill with a needle she had learned in her father's theatrical costumier establishment and she started to turn out handmade bridal headdresses, collections of which she sold to London – as well as Dublin – stores, including Harrods.

On the vast majority of the return trips, though, Eamonn was alone. But neither he nor Grainne ever had any worries that these weekly separations would tempt Eamonn into infidelity. However, and despite the journalist's comment early in his career that 'nobody could accuse him of having a dangerous quantity of sex appeal', a hire-car driver who for years chauffeured him to the 'This Is Your Life' studio believed differently.

On the journey there Eamonn always instructed him to take him first to a certain London hotel where, ever particular about his hair on programme day, he visited the barber's shop to have it trimmed.

One morning when he got back into the car the driver started to study him carefully in his rear-view mirror. Then he said, 'Do you mind me asking, Eamonn, but have you just had a haircut?'

Eamonn told him he had.

Said the driver, 'Blimey and all these years I've thought you were calling here because you were having a bit on the side!'

In his early days at the BBC there were stories linking his name with glamorous ladies of the day, and they persisted for a while after he joined Thames. He had plenty of opportunity to make extra-marital liaisons but if he did so he was extraordinarily careful. In nearly twenty-five years of working with him I never saw him do anything to cause even the corner of an eyebrow to be raised.

One of the most blatant attempts by a lady to get amorous with him was one night the chat show was produced not in its usual London studio, but in Newcastle upon Tyne.

She was a beautiful torch singer who was a guest on the programme. During the usual party afterwards, she never left Eamonn's side and kept linking his arm. Then, when he left, she managed, despite all his polite protests, to get into the car taking him back to his hotel.

When they arrived she seemed genuinely surprised when Eamonn told her that was as far as she was going and firmly bade her goodnight.

Just as well that he did. He found out next day that the singer was the mistress of a renowned criminal – who was then in prison after being convicted of a gangland murder.

Eamonn's apparent lack of interest in the ladies inevitably gave rise to other rumours that he was homosexual. These became very much more prevalent when he so quickly lost two or three stones in weight in the six months before he died and many people became convinced he was suffering from AIDS. That was not true, either, of course.

Some people who knew him well were convinced that, whether because of his religious upbringing, or an abhorrence of sex that was instilled or even beaten into him by the Christian Brothers, or because of his great love for his mother, Eamonn, whose spiritual inspiration was the Virgin Mary, had found the idea of sexual congress odious in his youth and – like the naivety of his childhood – that had stayed with him in adulthood. They believed that right throughout his life he was, in fact, asexual.

If Eamonn was ever going to stray it would have been in ultra-permissive New York City. He had been there many times and knew it well. Or should have done. I found it odd, however, that when on a working visit with him there in the mid-Seventies I referred to it as 'The Big Apple', the sobriquet given to it by show business people, he had no idea what I was talking about.

It was clear from that trip Eamonn had not been tempted by any illicit liaisons during those earlier visits or, if he had, he was too discreet to betray the fact. My belief, however, was that, just as at home, Eamonn was an innocent abroad.

We were in New York for three weeks during the last week of which Thames Television had taken over New York's Channel Nine. Their aim was to show American viewers what they considered to be the best of their own programmes, in the hope that sufficient interest would be created to persuade the American networks to buy some.

Eamonn's job specifically was to introduce a nightly magazine show of which I was editor – transmitted live by satellite link simultaneously in New York and London.

But if New York itself was a shock to the unsullied, there could have been no less likely a place for virtuous Eamonn to work than those New York studios.

They were situated close to the junction of Times Square and the notorious 42nd Street, no longer the street of dreams immortalised in the musical to which it gave its name but a tawdry thoroughfare of drug pushers and pimps and unhappy hookers hustling their wares outside pornographic cinemas, girlie peepshows and tatty theatres with hoardings screaming of live sex shows within.

If the members of that lost legion themselves had all put their heads together to choose a place of work for the upstanding Eamonn they could hardly have come up with anything more unsalubrious than the location of the studios of Channel Nine.

They were above one of the porn cinemas. But, considering the fact Eamonn had always been very religious minded, it was the particular piece of porn that was showing there that really added piquancy to the place.

From the huge lurid posters with which the foyer was festooned it was obviously about two young nuns who were demonstrably getting out of their old habits – including the ones they were wearing – and into some new and very kinky ones, as they became lay sisters in the then newest American connotation of the phrase.

There was little chance even Eamonn would confuse this film with 'The Sound Of Music' and I wondered what any visiting British tourists would have thought if they had happened to see him apparently going in to watch the antics of those naughty nuns every night for a week.

But it was inside that I had to save Eamonn from a greater shock.

On the day we arrived he was introduced to a young American researcher who was to work for Thames during its stay, a quiet-looking mouse of a girl to whom he took an instant liking.

In her tiny office afterwards she told me her ambition was to be a writer and handed me an immaculately typed manuscript.

I could hardly believe my eyes. What I started to read was the most explicit pornographic writing I had ever seen in my life.

She asked me what I thought of it and I said it was certainly pretty descriptive. Then Eamonn walked past her open door.

'I'll show it to the big guy,' said the girl, who had never heard of Eamonn before that day, and started after him with the manuscript. But I managed to stop her before she reached him and told her the star of the Thames week in New York would probably not share her enthusiasm for it.

It was an odd sensation to walk through the streets of New York with Eamonn after places like London where – unlike Paris! – taxi drivers called to him in familiar terms and passers-by occasionally thrust those 'grubby scraps of paper and stubs of pencils' at him for autographs.

Despite those appearances as a guest panellist on the American 'What's My Line?' over the years nobody in the city recognised him any more.

I sensed he was missing that and, in an odd way, I felt sorry for him.

Particularly when his face did not get him the immediate attention he usually got at home, as in a crowded New York bar one evening when the barman seemed determined not to let him catch his eye. Perhaps because he was so used to receiving celebrity service, Eamonn became visibly more and more impatient and his voice louder, the first and only time I ever witnessed that in public.

After what seemed a very long time the waiter finally turned to him. Not to serve him though. Instead, he looked Eamonn straight in the eye and, for the benefit of all those thirsty New Yorkers, said to him slowly and evenly, 'Just you wait your turn, bud! This ain't no tourist bar!'

For a moment, I suspected, all of Eamonn's old boxing instincts came rushing back, but he managed to swallow the rebuke and wait quietly fuming until the man finally condescended to serve him.

I also personally experienced in New York how irritated he could become when anybody else got a share of the limelight he thought belonged to him alone.

My own role in the city was twofold. Besides being editor of the magazine show I was also there as one of the principal writers of the drama series 'Man At The Top', based on John Braine's novels *Room At The Top* and *Life At The Top*, episodes of which Thames were also showing nightly in New York. It was a series which, had he ever acknowledged knowing about, I imagined Eamonn would have had little approval because its central character, Joe Lampton, was, by his lights – and most other people's – an amoral fornicator.

As a writer of the series I was asked to appear on a New York television programme. But, in the course of answering questions about Lampton's scandalous activities – the series was killed off in Britain after protests by self-appointed protector of our morals, Mrs Mary Whitehouse – I omitted to put in a word about Eamonn, or his magazine show.

When I met him afterwards the only reference he made to the programme was an acid, 'Thanks for the mention.'

Surprisingly, the bosses of New York's Channel Nine felt obliged to share Mrs Whitehouse's views on the series. Although the episodes were transmitted very late at night they decided to take down the sound on some of the fruitier things Lampton had to say.

In one exchange with his self-righteous father-in-law Lampton called out, 'Don't look at me as though I've just farted in church.'

The duty engineer, of course, faded out the sound on the word 'farted'. But, for some reason, the New York viewers, unfamiliar with the phrase, concluded that Lampton was denying having been up to another activity in church which began with the letter F. They bombarded both the Thames office and the Channel Nine studios with calls demanding to know if their assumptions had been correct.

It was not that the viewers were upset that Thames seemed prepared to assault their ears with such a sacrilegious suggestion, but that they were annoyed at Channel Nine for having prevented them from hearing it.

What those 'liberal-minded' viewers did not know – and nor did Thames, Channel Nine, and, fortunately, not Eamonn either – was that the following night they were to come within a matter of feet and of moments of witnessing a live television spectacular that would have brought the so-called 'unshockable city' to a complete standstill.

The cause was another New York lady with, apparently, the same predilictions as the young would-be porn-purveyor. She was a passionate Public Relations girl who decided she was going to have private relations with the one-time news reader, now disc jockey and quiz show host, David Hamilton, who was there to introduce the Thames's programmes.

And this particular public relations expert, who had been engaged by Thames for their stay, apparently did not mind if those private relations were in public, and on television, too.

In fact, it could have been that she wanted them to be seen on television, thereby creating some bizarre kind of record for which Norris McWhirter and his Guinness Book was not yet ready. A sort of television equivalent of the so-called Mile High club.

She had had designs on the Thames announcer from the moment he arrived in New York and, on his last night there she decided it was then or never.

That evening in the main studio Eamonn watched Hamilton on a monitor as he introduced the magazine programme from a fixed, remotely controlled camera in an announcer's booth in another part of the building. Fortunately, however, Eamonn was listening for the line with which Hamilton would cue the start of his show rather than looking carefully at him.

For suddenly Hamilton looked startled, even astonished, and there was a flash of panic in his eyes. Despite the very experienced broadcaster he was, he appeared to be gripping the edge of his desk as though fighting to keep his composure. He just about managed to do so until he finished introducing Eamonn and the camera faded him out.

The cause was the PR lady. She had been just out of sight of the camera's lens at the time viewers might have detected Hamilton's near loss of poise – under the desk, in fact.

Eamonn was to return to New York a few years later for the 'This Is Your Life' of London-born American-raised composer Jules Styne and was not endeared to it by the degree of recognition he got that time either.

During a run-through of the show one of the guests, the equally famous composer Stephen Sondheim, who had rushed in at the last minute to go over the contribution he was going to make, started to talk about a conversation he had once had about Styne with yet a third composer who, in fact, had not been invited to take part in the show.

Eamonn let him finish but after the run-through he drew Sondheim on one side and politely started to explain to him that in the British version of 'This Is Your Life' guests were urged not to mention people who were not appearing in case the subject took it as an indication they were about to come on and was disappointed when they did not.

Repeatedly glancing at his watch Sondheim listened with growing impatience and before Eamonn could finish he interrupted to deliver what was perhaps not the most lyrical line he has come out with in his songwriting career.

'Look,' he said to a startled Eamonn, 'don't tell me the fucking history of the show. Just tell me what you want me to say!'

Eamonn would have been mortified had he known about the liberties the liberated New York lady had taken during his earlier trip. He would have been equally shocked had he learned of some of the antics that went on around him on his demure, family show 'This Is Your Life' back home in London. As with all things likely to touch on his sensitivities they were very carefully kept from him, however.

Like the escapades of one married man on his team, and a closer friend of his than most, who had a lengthy and turbulent affair with one of the programme's secretaries without him ever suspecting.

Everybody else in the building knew about it, however. Some had even seen them engaged in their amorous activities – on a television screen.

So fierce was their passion that when work was finished for the day, not only could they not wait to get back to the secretary's flat, sometimes they could not even wait until they got to his car.

As many in the building were aware, the moment they hurried out of the lift into the basement car park they would look around to make sure there was nobody else about then drape themselves over the bonnet of one of the first cars they came to.

Thus the car park moved for both of them regularly until one evening when, all passion spent, the girl gazed dreamily about her from atop the bonnet of a Granada Ghia and saw something she had not spotted before – a television camera.

It was too late. The equivalent of a 'House Full' notice had been up in the security office on the floor above for nearly half-an-hour, as colleagues watched them on monitors linked to the newly installed security cameras.

Now they looked on with merriment as the couple frantically ducked and weaved between other cars as they tried to get out of camera-shot on their way to his.

Again because of the conspiracy of silence, Eamonn would frequently report, with some amusement, to the production meeting that the subject of the previous night's 'This Is Your Life' had told him afterwards that because his wife had been behaving oddly in the past few weeks he had started to suspect her of having an affair. Occasionally, however, the laughter which greeted that remark had a nervous edge to it, because, in fact, the wife *had* become more interested in researching the researcher than helping him research her husband.

Some female members of the team even talked in code to hide their amorous aspirations from Eamonn. Once he accidentally overheard one say to another as they were checking the script for the 'Life' of an international rugby player, 'There's lots of PLO in this show.'

'PLO? Doesn't that stand for Palestine Liberation Army?' he asked one of the researchers. 'What's that got to do with our show?'

The researcher told him he had no idea what the lady was talking about.

He could hardly tell him that, in that context, PLO stood for 'Potential Leg Over'. That was how some of the girls summed up the show's potential for romantic adventures. Some shows had little 'Potential Leg Over', but some had lots – mostly programmes about famous sportsmen onto which were usually invited all their teammates, club-mates, and the members of the international sides they played for.

Frequently there were as many as thirty young athletes – or pop stars, or celebrities away from their wives for the evening – to whom the girls would be playing hostess at the big and bibulous party after the show.

For Eamonn, the hour immediately after the show meant a welcome drink while he watched the just-recorded programme being played back on a monitor. If any passionate pursuits went on around him, he remained happily oblivious of them.

14

Things go down
in the drink

The odds against Eamonn repeating the gaffe he made on
the 'This Is Your Life' of Coco the Clown must have been
incalculable. But when the chat show with which he started
his ITV career was briefly revived in 1979, using the New London
Theatre as its studio, it – or something very like it – happened again.

On the programme the guests sat with him on the theatre's stage
and from that vantage point Eamonn, whenever he could find the
excuse, liked to talk to members of the audience below him in the
orchestra stalls and briefly involve them in the chat.

When he threw a question to the audience in one of the very
first of these shows he got an answer from a man sitting in the fourth
or fifth row and decided the viewers should have a better view of
him.

So he called to him to stand up. The man made no move. So
Eamonn asked him a second time. 'Come on, stand up for the
cameras so everyone at home can see you,' he called.

The man still did not move but said something Eamonn could
not hear.

So he called out even louder, 'What was that? Come on, stand
up so we can all see you. Come on, now! Up! Up! Up!'

It was at that point the man's daughter, who was sitting beside
him, shouted back, 'He's telling you he can't stand up. He's got no
legs.'

That, unfortunately for Eamonn was the kind of embarrassment that dogged the ill-considered decision by Thames Television – where memories must have been short – to revive 'The Eamonn Andrews Show'. It was a complete flop and lasted only three months.

Echoes of his original chat show came at the very start of the revival. Playwright and barrister John Mortimer, author of the television series 'Rumpole Of The Bailey' was talking about a visit he had recently made to Thailand and made a sly reference to a 'Bangkok sandwich'.

This brought a ribald laugh from those people in the audience who knew it was something on the menu in Bangkok brothels, or so called massage parlours, for which the services of two prostitutes were required, and not something bought at a sandwich bar.

Eamonn realised what Mortimer had said must have been a little risqué but had no idea why. However, his instincts told him to change the subject immediately. Which he did by leaping in to say, 'Well, John, whether you have your sandwich in Bangkok or in Birmingham ...'

This was greeted by an even greater guffaw from the audience which mystified Eamonn even further. But it did not tempt him to risk further discomfort after the show by asking Mortimer to explain the cause of the laughter when they had a drink together in the hospitality room.

They did however talk more about Thailand and Mortimer's description of the country inspired Eamonn, two years later, to choose it as an uncharacteristically adventurous holiday destination for Grainne and himself to celebrate a trio of anniversaries which all occurred that year – forty years in radio and thirty years since the start of both his television career and their marriage.

However, nobody ever learned if, while he was there, he found out precisely to what Mortimer had been alluding – either in the way some male tourists do or by attempting to order a Bangkok sandwich in the hotel coffee shop.

Shortly after Eamonn arrived in Bangkok there was an attempted military coup. British television and newspapers showed pictures of soldiers and tanks taking to the streets and outbreaks of fighting all over the city. So serious was the situation that the King fled his strongly guarded palace for the greater safety of a mountain retreat.

In London, having had no word from the star of their show,

members of the production team of 'This Is Your Life', were becoming concerned for his safety. So the producer decided to try to contact him.

He spent hour after hour on the telephone but the situation in Bangkok was chaotic. Then, some time after three o'clock in the morning, exhausted but relieved, he heard Eamonn's voice at the other end of the line.

However, before he could get out more than a few words of greeting, Eamonn, to his astonishment, started to berate him for disturbing him while he was on holiday.

'But,' the producer protested, 'the reason I phoned was we were all worried about you because of the revolution.'

To which, betraying not a lot of the perception and eloquence normally acquired in four decades of broadcasting and journalism, Eamonn replied, 'What shaggin' revolution!'

The producer, understandably was very much taken aback and not a little offended. He shrugged it off, however.

For one thing, considering Eamonn's apparent, ever-puzzling determination to remain detached from, even totally indifferent to, events that occurred in the world around him, the fact that he was oblivious to a minor revolution being fought outside his holiday hotel was hardly a matter for much amazement.

There was also the possibility Eamonn's irritability had been due to duty free gin. There were often times when the 'pillar of television', as one of the obituaries described him, needed quite a bit of propping up.

Perhaps it was because of the pressures of trying to revive 'The Eamonn Andrews Show' while still carrying on with 'This Is Your Life' and the 'Today' shows, but around that time Eamonn started to drink even more heavily than he normally did.

He did most of his drinking when he was alone in his flat in Chiswick or in the study of his house in Ireland.

Senior members of his programme production teams were familiar with his study at Chiswick because they were frequently summoned there. It was decorated in a vivid orange colour, rather like a nuclear explosion in the Kalahari Desert, and, without the knowledge of himself, or Grainne whom he said had designed it, they called it 'the satsuma suite'.

When well fortified by the alcohol, he would pick up the phone and, often for more than an hour at a time, would have a slurred-speech, largely incomprehensible conversation, late into the night, with the luckless victim at the other end.

These diatribes – for, sadly, they were little less – mostly consisted of carping criticisms of a script or a programme's contents, and to escape from having to listen to his outpourings some of the more experienced of his back-up team kept the telephone answering machines at their homes switched on all the time.

When they recognised the voice of a friend calling they switched off the tape and answered. When they heard Eamonn's intoxicated tone they let him believe the tape when it told him there was nobody home.

The effect that drinking had on him was especially evident at 'This Is Your Life' production meetings, when he referred to the copious notes he had scrawled on scripts during those sessions in his study, always in green (for his Irishness) ink. Very often he found he could not even understand them, remember why he wrote them, or was even able to decipher them.

In his notes, when he was able to interpret them, he frequently expressed vehement and sarcastic dislike for a line in the script. Equally frequently what nobody dare tell him was that the line he was ridiculing was often one he had himself dictated to the writer or producer during his previous telephone call and insisted should be put in the script in place of an existing one.

At the meeting he would then go on to suggest an alternative line for the one he had forgotten he had himself rewritten, and the writer would usually be quick to accept it. That was because he had now changed the line back to the way the writer had written it in the first place.

In much the same way, he would demand that whole 'This Is Your Life' scripts be rewritten as often as six to ten times – the record was seventeen – and frequently there would be little difference between the one he finally accepted and the first one he had so decisively rejected.

It may have been the drinking or it may have been that without anybody realising it he was already starting to feel the effects of the heart disease that was to cause his death, but in his last years he began to show the blacker side of his nature more frequently and more indiscreetly.

He would often snarl at his colleagues and sneeringly address a producer or director as 'Mister-technical-fucking-genius'. Once during rehearsals, for which he usually wore comfortable old carpet slippers, one of the production team happened to mention that the playwright Alun Owen, who, naturally, did most of his writing at home, had once been quoted as saying he could not start work if he was still wearing his slippers.

Whereupon, in a rare public display of arrogance, Eamonn snapped back, 'Is that so! Well, you can if you're a *star*!'

It was reported at the time that he had sacked a lifelong friend, who for years had managed most of his businesses in Ireland, while the man was on his back recovering from open heart surgery. As he was then frequently beginning to show the uncaring streak some had suspected was in him since he had displayed only indifference to the deaths of the four Derbyshire villagers involved in the pilot of his original chat show, that was not too difficult to believe.

At the script meeting for Patrick McNee's 'This Is Your Life' a researcher said it was unlikely the usually impassive actor would show any of the emotion which was practically considered to be an essential ingredient to make the programme a success.

By chance, Eamonn had just heard McNee say in a radio interview that the saddest time of his life had been in wartime when, on the one day he was on sick leave, the torpedo boat on which he was serving was sunk and he had lost every one of his shipmates.

So, when he heard the researcher's remarks, Eamonn picked up a photograph of McNee taken at that time and said, 'I know how to get a tear out of him. I'll push this picture in front of his face and say, "Now weep you bastard! Weep!"'

When the programme on the veteran actor and founder of 'The Mermaid Theatre', Lord Miles, ran nearly twice its allotted time, it was decided to postpone its transmission until it could be given a longer than normal slot in the Christmas schedules.

But that also made the production team nervous. Christmas was still nearly three months away and, because of the ages of most of them, they feared that by then one or two of the guests on that 'This Is Your Life' might have departed this life. For apart from the subject, who was then seventy-seven years old, and his wife, who was about the same age, on the show were also an older sister of Lord Miles, friends who were aged seventy-six and eighty, and opera singer Dame Eva Turner, who was ninety-two.

But when the fear was aired that one, or even more, might pass away before transmission, Eamonn simply shrugged and said, 'I'm not worried. It will be worth it for the publicity.'

Sadly, one of the guests did die before the programme went on the air. But, ironically, he was not one of the very elderly ones but, in fact, the guest who – had the question been asked – would have been considered to have been about the fittest, fifty-seven-year-old actor Leonard Rossiter. Rossiter, who was reputed to be one of the finest amateur squash players in Britain, died suddenly in his dressing room during a West End revival of Joe Orton's black comedy 'Loot'.

Ironically, too, although on the programme he delivered 'a polite piece' about Lord Miles, Rossiter had accepted the invitation to take part with bad grace, claiming that he had learned nothing about acting during his lengthy association with him but rather that the reverse was the case.

A few months after the Lord Miles programme, members of the production team were also somewhat startled to hear an outburst from Eamonn about Bob Geldof's baby daughter when he presented his 'This Is Your Life'. The child's mother, Paula Yates, wanted her to be brought on as the climax to the show because she thought nothing would move Geldof more.

Eamonn told the girl researcher who reported this that he did not like the idea.

Said the researcher: 'But she's a real cute little thing.'

Said Eamonn: 'It's the ugliest baby I have ever seen in my life. Ugly! Ugly! Ugly!'

The reseacher tried again. 'She's wearing a cute little sailor suit,' she said.

Replied Eamonn: 'Then I hope that sailor hat's pulled well down over its fucking face!'

Another reason Eamonn no longer had the strength of mind to subdue the outbursts that betrayed that side of his nature was possibly because he was now very much preoccupied with business worries.

As early as 1962, two years before he started hiring his services out to the bigger spending paymasters of ITV, newspapers reported that he was earning three times as much as the BBC's then Director-

General, Hugh Carleton-Greene, and his manager was quoted as saying, 'He is now so rich money no longer matters to him.'

Whether money mattered to him or not, he still went on making more and more of it. Besides his lucrative BBC contracts, he was signed up for a series of commercials for a brand of toothpaste – although, ironically, he was plagued by tooth trouble for most of his life – and, in addition to his columns in the London evening paper, *The Star* and the *Catholic Herald*, he made frequent contributions to two Sunday newspapers, the *Sunday Dispatch* and *Empire News* and also to *Punch*.

Then there were the companies he owned or in which he held directorships and at the peak of his wealth he was reckoned to be a millionaire several times over.

Apart from his two homes, the mansion in Ireland, which in 1980 was estimated to be worth more than £500,000, and his spacious apartment in Chiswick, he had companies in Ireland which owned a hotel, a country club, a theatre, a nightclub, recording studios, an investment company and a theatrical agency. He also had an investment company in the Bahamas. In addition, he had been appointed director of Butlins in 1970 and of Securicor (Ireland) in 1972.

His business fortune began in Dublin in the Fifties when with a brother-in-law he started the Eamonn Andrews Studios to make sponsored programmes for Radio Eireann and which later went into the pop music recording business and television commercials. After that, in England, he became a partner in the theatrical agency of which he had once been a client and in a music publishing business.

He then got his first financial fright which came because, in 1964, he took his first ITV contract to Arbiter and Weston, a company dealing in bowling alleys and nightclubs, in return for shares and a seat on the board. Four years later the company went into liquidation.

It was odd for someone who hardly ever stepped inside one that nightclubs should figure so largely in Eamonn's business life and – besides the Arbiter and Weston fiasco – that it should have been a nightclub that finally brought it all crashing down.

It was a floating nightclub, in fact an expensively refitted Scottish ferryboat, which a subsidiary company of the Eamonn Andrews Studios launched on the River Liffey in June, 1983. Ironically the venture was also his own idea and one he came up with many months after business colleagues had begged him to hand over the running of the companies to others with more time to attend to them.

That apart, perhaps Eamonn should have more carefully noted the name of the vessel, and looked on it as an omen, because it was called the Arran, the same name as the Earl who almost sank his chat show, too, with his discourse on balls and strawberry leaves.

Even the bottle of champagne used at the launching resisted all of Grainne's efforts to smash it against the bows.

Had Eamonn's company – fifty percent of the money was from other investors – simply poured its cash straight into the Liffey, instead of bothering to launch the Arran on to it, it could scarcely have lost it quicker. Within seven months, through the total lack of interest of the Dublin glitterati, the whole venture had foundered and had dragged all of Eamonn's other businesses under the waves with it.

The nightclub's debts alone were reported in Dublin High Court to be more than £500,000 with assets of only £161, but his saddest day was Friday the 13th of January, 1984, when a receiver moved into the place where his business ambitions had first taken root thirty years before, the Eamonn Andrews Studios.

However, despite the hysterical headlines about his losses, Eamonn, it transpired, had been too cautious as to expose too much of his own wealth to the floating nightclub venture.

In the weeks after the liquidators were called in members of the 'This Is Your Life' team naturally avoided any mention of these events in his presence. But Eamonn finally ended the tension at a meeting two months later when he said, 'You have all been discreetly silent about the stories of my business affairs in recent weeks and I respect you for that.

'However, if I may paraphrase Mark Twain, I would now like to say that reports of my debt have been greatly exaggerated.'

Despite all the wheeling and dealing in which he was involved in his business life, Eamonn was nervous about handling money or writing cheques himself, and at the start of each week Grainne would give him an envelope containing £50 'pocket-money'.

She once remarked that in matters of money, as in other facets of life, he was 'so naive', by which she meant he had little idea of what things cost.

Even up to the time of his death, when Emma was twenty-six and working in public relations with a Dublin hotel, Fergal twenty-three and a rock group musician, and nineteen-year-old Niamh was a children's nurse, he would still occasionally question them about how much they had spent on articles of clothing and they would have to pretend they had paid far less for them than was the case. If he had known a sweater had really cost three times the £4 he had been told he would have been shocked and insisted that it be taken back to the shop.

'It might have been £40, or even £400, but he did not ask any more questions.' Grainne was quoted as saying shortly after his death.

She also said, 'He did once take me to a costume jewellery shop and bought me a huge diamanté necklace and bracelet. There was this strange look on his face and I realised he thought he'd paid for real diamonds.'

He might have been naive about money in his family's eyes but his colleagues saw him as someone who, not unlike many other successful people in show business, was very careful with his cash.

Doubtless it was a genuine oversight when, in 1971, he failed to pay his £50 annual subscription to Royal Mid-Surrey Golf Club until he was named as a defaulter in a notice displayed in the club house for all to see, and then resigned his four-year membership.

But it was a fact that he washed his own hair before visiting the barber to save paying for a shampoo and, besides putting optics on his spirit bottles, during the days he lived in the large house at Chiswick, he also smoked a cheap brand of cigarettes because the makers sent them to him free, hoping people seeing somebody so famous smoking them would be sufficiently impressed to try them themselves.

For a number of years he used to make the producers and directors of his programmes Christmas gifts of food and wine hampers. The hamper intended for the producer, a more influential person than the director, was always a little more expensive and he identified them as 'Hamper A' and 'Hamper B' on a list he gave to the studio assistant he made responsible for distributing all of his Yuletide largesse.

The system worked well until one Christmas a director found his usual two bottles of wine had been upgraded to champagne and told Eamonn how well they had washed down the turkey. Eamonn then realised, to his discomfort, that the assistant had got the hampers mixed and that year the producer must have ended up with the less sumptuous 'Hamper B'.

From then on, to his chagrin, he had to go to the extra expense of providing hampers which both contained champagne rather than ordinary wine. Fortunately, however, only a couple of Christmases later a change in programme personnel gave him the opportunity to drop the idea of hampers altogether.

At Christmas each female member of his programme production team received a bottle of champagne while each male got a bottle of a gin distilled in Eire. The wife of one senior member of the team was so contemptuous of it when her husband first arrived with his bottle of Cork gin he never dared take one home again. Year after year for more than a decade he stuffed it, still in its Christmas wrapping, in the first drawer he found unlocked in any adjacent office for some surprised secretary to discover in the New Year.

To one of his colleagues who joined him in an executive capacity when he first went to ITV, Eamonn originally gave Christmas boxes of splendid pieces of Waterford glass. Later when the man took a slightly less responsible role on the team he relegated him to the Irish gin league.

Then, finally, when changing circumstances meant his contribution to the programme was restricted to writing half-a-dozen scripts for each series, Eamonn also crossed him off the gin list and sent him a Christmas card instead.

An enduring memento of his cautiousness over cash was the powder blue Mercedes coupé that was standing on the drive of his home in Ireland the day he died. It was a car he bought in 1962 to celebrate signing his most lucrative and, as it transpired, last contract with the BBC, one that brought him in a then headline-making £30,000 a year.

Outside of the Rolls range, it was one of the dearest cars on the market at the time and having paid so much for it he seemed to expect it to last for ever.

But, to his intense annoyance, he found that after a mere twenty years its flooring was in need of some repair and, because the model had long been out of production, his local Mercedes specialists were unable to carry it out. The car seemed destined for the scrap yard.

However, when a colleague heard this he volunteered that a neighbour of his was a senior executive with Mercedes Benz in Britain and offered to seek his assistance.

Eamonn asked him to do so right away and, later, the colleague was able to tell him the car *could* be repaired, though only at the principal Mercedes workshops in Stuttgart, West Germany.

But the really good news he was delighted to pass on was that once the repairs had been carried out it would be an extremely valuable motor car. The company executive had also told him that very few of that particular model Mercedes had been produced and that had given Eamonn's a tremendous rarity value.

So the car went off to Germany and in due course it was returned, and is now a prized collector's item.

The colleague expected Eamonn to be pleased. But he was furious. 'The bastards sent me a bill,' he exploded.

He had genuinely believed that, like smoking the free cigarettes, Mercedes would have considered that by being seen driving the car he was giving their product some extra kudos. And for that reason they should have enabled him to do that at their own expense.

He was, in fact, so furious about having to pay the bill he never even thanked the colleague for the trouble he had gone to but for months actually treated him as though he was responsible for costing him the money.

By the time his business empire started to totter – and he would have had some reason to be upset about paying a large bill for the car – Eamonn was also becoming more and more anxious about his career because he was still presenting only one programme for Thames although, at his insistence, he had a two-show contract.

The truth was that, ironically, the phenomenal success of 'This Is Your Life' made him feel a failure. He desperately wanted to succeed with another show to prove that he was not just a one-programme man.

The real problem, although he probably did not recognise it, was that he had only ever succeeded with either a programme that required practically nothing by way of a script, as with 'What's My Line?', or one which permitted him to read practically every word of the script quite openly – because it was all there in 'the book' – as 'This Is Your Life' did.

Unfortunately no other programme he tried had these built-in safeguards and with all of them he was less successful, if not a disaster.

On the magazine programme 'Today', which he presented on average three nights a week for ten years, his duties were mostly those of link-man with autocue to safeguard him, although during that time he also did a number of fairly straightforward interviews.

It was also purely a regional show, albeit the important London region, and as such he did not rate it as an alternative to the nationally shown 'This Is Your Life'. He was prepared to work on it only until another network chance came along.

'Time For Business', his next programme, was not it. The City-orientated show ran two brief seasons with Eamonn – who in his own biography had declared 'I have never seen myself as the bowler hat type' – sitting uneasily in the chair.

So, after the return of his chat show had been a flop, too, he went back to where he had begun when his attempts at a more challenging acting and writing career had failed in his early days in Dublin. He returned to variations of the kind of show that had given him his start on the stage and in both radio and television – the quiz show.

He tried two very different ones. The first was one that combined the slapstick 'It's A Knockout' with the cerebral 'Mastermind' – with opposing teams scoring points for physical agility as well as brain power – and to test its feasibility Thames TV mounted a hugely expensive pilot programme in a London sports stadium.

And it seemed they were about to have a big success on their hands as, amidst a fanfare of trumpets, Eamonn mounted a specially designed podium in front of a grandstand packed with the favour-sporting supporters of sides representing two London boroughs – with all the leading civic dignatories of both occupying two 'royal boxes' – and who were being whipped up to fever pitch by troupes of pretty, American-style drum-majorettes and cheerleaders.

On the podium, too, or standing beside the elaborate sets that surrounded it, and with every conceivable kind of sports gear, were thirty contestants – all selected as a result of months of painstaking research.

Specially transported to the stadium, too, were five television cameras, a mobile control gallery, make-up and wardrobe departments, dressing rooms, a catering unit, electric generators, property vehicles, and a fleet of cars. And, of course, the complement of around fifty highly paid people who went with them.

It was not going to be a mere melding of 'Mastermind' and 'It's A Knockout', it was going to be more dramatic than one, more spectacular than the other.

Until Eamonn dealt the whole dazzling enterprise a knockout blow.

The show itself went better than could have been hoped for. Soon the teams were neck and neck, and with the excitement mounting they stayed that way right to the end. It could not have been better, two perfectly matched teams in a dead heat to set up a dramatic play-off.

Then the programme hit an unexpected snag. Eamonn had not taken the trouble to memorise the rules – including the one carefully worked out to allow for the contingency of a play-off. So, to the amazement and consternation of both the production team and the players, he simply made up one of his own. Well, not exactly a rule, more an anticlimax.

In the final challenge of the contest players had been demonstrating their skills with soccer balls.

Suddenly Eamonn shouted: 'The first player to kick a ball to me decides which side wins.'

The programme team could not believe their ears. Nor could the spectators.

And nor could the contestants. They *knew* the rules allowed for a play-off. They simply looked at each other in bewilderment.

So Eamonn shouted his newly minted rule again. Then a third time. Finally it dawned on the contestant standing a little nearer the podium than anybody else that he must win such an unequal race. With nothing to lose he set off for the podium with a football at his feet.

And, as the opposing side's supporters jeered in derision, Eamonn announced that that particular contestant's side were the winners.

Then, while the 'losing' side continued to protest, he leapt from the podium, dashed across the running track and disappeared into his mobile dressing room.

Shortly afterwards, and still totally unclear as to what had happened, the spectators started to drift away. Later, Thames Television wiped off the whole shambles as a dead loss.

But by comparison with Eamonn's next quiz cock-up that one had cost peanuts.

'Top Of The World', was a contest of knowledge in which he was linked to a contestant in another London studio and by satellite to others in the USA and Australia, competing for the richest ever first prize in a British television programme – a vintage Rolls Royce cabriolet.

When it was announced that Eamonn was going to be the question master, a journalist asked if he could test him on his own general knowledge. Eamonn reluctantly agreed.

'Who was the first President of the United States?' the reporter asked.

Eamonn thought for a moment. 'Er, was it Grant?' he proffered.

Then, in answer to a couple more questions, he got Armistice Day fourteen days late, saying it was November 25, and the American Declaration of Independence fourteen years late, at 1790, before putting an end to all this mind-bending stuff by rightly pointing out it was his job to ask the questions not answer them.

Thames were so proud of their idea to make a vintage Rolls the first prize because, as its value was a matter of speculation, it cunningly got round the IBA's then prize money limit of £1,750. To emphasise the point, they announced it as 'something money can't buy', which prompted a newspaper to raise the question: 'Did they steal it then?'

Rolls or not, Eamonn's ride as quiz master was far from smooth. With such a valuable prize as that at stake – it was estimated to be worth at least £60,000 – and the tension mounting, it really was not very smart of him suddenly to interrupt the proceedings to tell an American woman contestant she had her 'pretty nose in front' and then attempt to continue the questioning.

As a result of flippancies like that, critics in three continents went after him.

The critic of one of Australia's most influential newspapers wrote: '"Top Of The World" is a great quiz show marred only by the ineptness of compère Eamonn Andrews.

'His endless fumblings prove that, though he is one of the most popular and highly paid performers on English television, he is remarkably inarticulate.

'Every time he opened his mouth the audience laughed'.

Broadcast magazine described it as the best unintentional comedy series on television.

In a reference to the quiz masters of 'Mastermind' and 'University Challenge' and a comedian famous for talking in his own version of gobbledegook, it said: 'Eamonn is no Magnus. He is no Bamber. Stanley Unwin he rivals.

'Eamonn finds long words difficult. Worse, Eamonn can't even read. Even when he gets it right he makes it sound wrong.

'The whole shooting match is a glee-inducing catastrophe.'

With notices like those it was little wonder that, after only one series, 'Top Of The World' came crashing down around him.

During the preparation work for that programme, Eamonn demonstrated two of the fundamental features of his make-up which made him a success in his career but which sensibly he kept well hidden from his admirers throughout it, his ability to place self-interest above any considerations of sentiment and the lengths to which he was prepared to go to protect his public image.

The first pilot of 'Top Of The World' was a failure, so Thames decided to mount a second. This time, however, two members of the 'This Is Your Life' production team heard from friends inside the company that the format to be used was, if not the same, then very similar to one they had themselves submitted a year earlier.

They raised the matter with Eamonn, with whom they had been closely associated for fifteen years. But he refused to talk about it, pointing out that he never discussed details of one programme with people who were connected with another.

However, after the pilot had been made they managed to see a video tape of it. It convinced them that, apart from a change in title – theirs had been 'Transworld Challenge' – it was their format. As they were not staff members but were on freelance contracts, this meant that if the company made a series they were entitled to royalty payments.

Thames management, however, claimed that any similarity between their format and the pilot was pure coincidence. They said it had been devised by members of Thames staff although they declined to name them.

They also announced their intention to go ahead with a series. So the two 'This Is Your Life' team members decided their only hope of getting the royalties to which they felt entitled was to enlist Eamonn as an ally.

As he refused to talk about it, they wrote to tell him they were convinced the format of the big new satellite programme he was about to launch (and which could now make him a star in America and Australia as well as Britain) was theirs. They asked if he would intercede with the company for them.

They heard nothing. It was, of course, possible their letter had been lost in the post. So they wrote again, and to make absolutely certain it reached him they slipped a copy of it into his overcoat pocket at a 'This Is Your Life' production meeting.

But again there was no response, not even an acknowledgement. Eamonn, they concluded, had decided he was not going to risk his own good relations with the Thames management by interceding on their behalf. Ultimately they were compelled to take their grievance to an adjudication committee set up by the Independent Television Companies Association from whom they eventually accepted a cash award equivalent to the royalties they would have received from one series – which, due in some measure to Eamonn's blunders, was all the programme was destined to run, anyway.

The question of an adjudicator was one that also occupied Eamonn's mind before 'Top Of The World' started its brief journey into space.

This one, however, was required for the programme itself, and totally necessary with such a rich prize at stake. But the problem was how the adjudicator's decision was to be conveyed to Eamonn. The producer presumed he would wear a microphone earpiece in the normal way, and as he had done for years taking instructions from Angus Mckay on 'Sports Report'.

But that was radio and he was not seen by the public to need such assistance. As, despite his poor eyesight, he had always refused to be seen wearing glasses on television, he was not going to be seen wearing an earpiece, either.

So another solution had to be found. Eventually, it was decided a member of the production team would wear the earpiece. He would crouch at Eamonn's feet, hidden from the viewers by the lectern from which he would ask the questions, and convey the adjudicator's rulings to him by a series of signals – one pull of his trouser leg for an acceptance, two pulls for a refusal.

Despite this strange but otherwise sound signalling system, Eamonn still, sadly, told an American semi-finalist one of his answers was wrong when in fact it was right, and eliminated him from the contest.

Thames had to apologise to the contestant for the mistake a few days later and give him back his place in the finals.

There was no fairy tale ending for him, though. He finished a runner-up.

Sad for him maybe, but perhaps just as well for Eamonn and what remained of the image he had tried so hard to protect throughout the series.

15

What Ali really said
about Eamonn

While he continued to be frustrated in his attempts to come across an alternative successful programme, Eamonn found himself having to work harder and harder – and to push the production team equally hard – to help ensure the survival of his one constant salary earner and insurance, 'This Is Your Life'.

To achieve that with a programme that had started three decades before meant trawling an ever-widening area for subjects and, even more important for the vital 'surprise' at the start of each show, for new and different audience-gripping locations, Paris, Rome, New York and Hollywood.

The first to take him beyond the British Isles was the 'Life' of the man who started the East African Flying Doctor Service, Dr Michael Wood, and even apart from the remoteness of the vast territory in which he worked, there was never any question that he might know the programme's plans in advance.

Dr Wood had then spent twenty years giving medical treatment to the nomadic Masai tribe in Kenya and had never seen the programme. More than that, he had never even heard of Eamonn Andrews.

So when Eamonn popped up in the middle of the bush, with a large red book on which the doctor's name was written in gold, he was totally bemused by the mysterious behaviour of this stranger, who, from his accent, he took to be an Irishman. However, he was eventually persuaded to go with him to an airport and fly to London to take part in a mysterious ritual there which they called 'This Is Your Life'.

When they arrived back at the studios, the team themselves had some doctoring to do – on the scene-setting shots they had filmed in the bush.

One of them was of a village head man emerging from his hut. However, the grass skirt he was wearing was not as decorously arranged as it might have been and there was more of him emerging than could be shown on British television at 7 pm.

As the programme notched up more and more years, film and tape doctoring was to play an increasing role in deciding how many a 'This Is Your Life' eventually looked and sounded.

But there was much more to 'improving the product' than that. These 'improvements' eventually were to include every single aspect of the programme from the 'pick-up' to the 'pay-off'.

When it came to the business of 'beefing up' a show, Eamonn's experience and expertise were invaluable. And often a source of wonder to newcomers to the production team.

In fact, he was a veritable sorcerer at making a silk purse out of a sow's ear of a programme, and there were sow's ears aplenty in his final few years.

Some doctoring operations were major, some minor.

Both major and minor surgery were required to save the 'Life' of film actress, Diana Dors.

Only a snip of the scissors was required to prevent viewers hearing how she reacted when the book was thrust at her for the second time in her life. She responded by yelling out to an audience of onlookers, 'Oh, no! Eamonn's Chamber of Horrors!'

But more major surgery was required to repair a part of the programme in which Eamonn said he was about to show her a message from her two sons, by her second marriage to comedian Dickie Dawson, which they had filmed at their home in Hollywood. As the actress watched the monitor screen in joyous anticipation Eamonn suddenly told her, and the audience, that the film had been 'lost'.

That was not true. When the production team had looked at it they had seen that although the two young men had stuck to the 'warm words' a 'Life' writer had prepared for them to say to their mother, they had used offensive gestures as they had delivered them to the camera. In fact, by their demeanour they were totally deriding the programme and the whole occasion.

It was decided the film could not be shown. So Eamonn had the idea that on the show he would appear to 'discover' at the very last moment that there was no film but in its place the producer had hastily arranged a transatlantic telephone message from them.

This was possible because, of course, the words they had used were perfectly acceptable. So the film sound-track was played and electronically made to sound like a transatlantic phone call.

When one of the team dared to suggest to Eamonn before he engaged in this sleight-of-hand that it was a lie to say the film had been lost when it was, in fact, there in the control gallery, he angrily replied with another of his puzzling remarks.

'The word "lost" doesn't mean lost,' he said. 'It means ... anything!'

In view of what happened when she was the subject of a 'Life' for the first time, during the programme's BBC days, it was surprising that Diana Dors agreed to let Eamonn take her through this second 'Life' at all.

Shortly before the BBC version she herself was living in Hollywood with her first husband, the flamboyant, often violent entrepreneur Dennis Hamilton. While they were there they threw a party round the pool of their Beverly Hills home to introduce a friend of theirs, London's then most fashionable hair-stylist, Mr 'Teasy-Weasy' Raymond, to the Hollywood set.

Mingling with the 'stars' at the party was also a photographer who realised he would be able to get some very saleable pictures of the film industry's latest 'sex-goddess' if somebody happened to push her into the pool fully clothed.

And as nobody seemed inclined to do that, he did so himself. However, as Miss Dors was being hauled from the water, Hamilton, who allowed nobody but himself to exploit his wife's publicity value, caught the photographer and beat him up quite badly.

So, when the BBC producers decided it would be a good gimmick to invite the photographer, Stewart Sawyer, to meet the actress on her 'This Is Your Life' to 'kiss and make up', they were surprised when both he and Hamilton agreed.

However, at the party after the show Hamilton became so beligerent towards Sawyer again that Miss Dors had to restrain him from beating him up a second time. The result was that, later, he vented his frustration on her and, not for the first time, she took a beating from him instead. They were divorced not long after millions of viewers had seen them so tenderly holding hands throughout the programme.

Sadly, it was not the only time tensions created by 'This Is Your Life' have led to family disputes.

American film actress Faye Dunaway and her then husband, English photographer Terry O'Neil, had such a row over dinner immediately after he had been the programme's subject that reportedly they cleared the Knightsbridge restaurant where they were eating. They, too, were divorced soon after the programme.

Even those famous heart-touching reunions, one of the programme's greatest rating attractions, have frequently been the cause of bitter family acrimony, especially when those 'long lost' relatives the programme has brought from some obscure point on the map have refused to go back there again and have still been cluttering up the subject's home weeks, sometimes months, later and paying neither board nor rent.

The mother of film actress Patricia Neal was only too glad to get back to her home in America, though, when the programme brought her over for her daughter's 'Life'.

At that time Miss Neal was married to writer Roald Dahl and living at Great Missenden, Buckinghamshire. After the programme Dahl, whose relationship with his mother-in-law had always been antagonistic, did not invite her to stay with them. It was a fact that their four children were home on holiday at the time and the house was rather full, but mum-in-law took it as a personal slight and wrote to her daughter to say so. All she got for her trouble was an even more scathing letter from Dahl himself. Dahl and Neal were to be divorced also, but that was five years later so 'This Is Your Life', or its aftermath, could hardly be blamed in that case.

Eamonn, however, for one brief period, thought it had been the cause of the break-up of the marriage of comedian Jim Davidson and his wife, Julie.

After the programme, Londoner Davidson insisted that all of his family and friends should go off to his favourite pub in the Old Kent Road for a party and when his wife pleaded that she was too tired after the events of the day he became very angry.

So angry in fact that when they finally got to their home in Sunningdale in the early hours of the morning, and although she had acquiesced and gone to the party, he leapt from the car, ran into the house and locked her out. She had to waken friends living nearby and spend the rest of the night with them. When Eamonn heard of this at a programme meeting he cried, 'Oh no! Don't tell me we've ruined another marriage!'

He was being a little hard on the programme because although they *were* divorced not long afterwards she was his second wife and within a couple of years Davidson had married and quickly been divorced by yet a third.

As if the unfortunate Diana Dors had not gone through enough after her first 'This Is Your Life', she had to endure yet another family rift after the second one. Not surprisingly the cause was her two sons from Hollywood who spent a few days after the programme at her home with her third husband, the actor Alan Lake and her son by that marriage. Almost inevitably there were frequent bitter quarrels and it was with great relief that she eventually saw them off on a plane back home to California.

By the show's standards, Eamonn's ruse to make those sons at least polite to their mother was not a big deception. Whole film contributions were sometimes added after the programme had been recorded and the first time the subject saw them was when he or she was watching it at home weeks later.

Eamonn came up with this idea in the early Seventies on the day of the taping of the 'Life' of featherweight boxing champion Alan Rudkin when an important piece of film featuring a Japanese boxer, and one of Rudkin's opponents, who called himself 'Fighting Harada', was frustratingly delayed by customs at Heathrow airport and destined to miss the recording.

Rather than be denied that contribution Eamonn decided to carry on as though it *was* in the show, except that when he reached the point in the script at which he should have introduced the film, he stopped the recording.

Then he explained to Rudkin – and the studio audience – exactly where the film was and that it would be inserted into the recorded show in time for transmission. After that he simply addressed a blank monitor screen with the words 'Thank you "Fighting Harada" in

Tokyo,' and carried on with the programme.

The idea worked well. So well, in fact, that the 'Fighting Harada', as it was henceforward called, was gradually extended into becoming a process by which, to 'beef-up' 'This Is Your Life' programmes, additional film inserts were shot after the show had been recorded.

The 'Life' of actor Brian Blessed was just one which was 'given an injection' by that method. Despite the reply 'Is he dead?' given by Sir John Gielgud when he was invited to appear on the programme, Blessed was still very much alive when it was made. But Eamonn decided there was not enough life in his 'This Is Your Life'.

He learned from research that Blessed had appeared in a television series, 'Master of Ballantrae', with rather more 'glamorous' actor Michael York. He demanded that York must be persuaded to put in an appearance.

There was one slight snag, however. At that time York was travelling to India and out of any kind of reach, and because of the perennial dearth of programmes 'in the can' there was no question of postponing.

That did little to daunt Eamonn, however. During the show's recording, after a clip from 'Master of Ballantrae', he told Blessed that York had sent him his best wishes for the programme from India.

Then, after the show, a crew managed to pin York down long enough for him to film a contribution. Eamonn then recorded an introduction to it and paid it off with himself looking at a monitor and saying 'Thank you Michael York in India', as though it was happening on the programme itself.

It must have come as a surprise to the studio audience when they watched the programme transmitted and not only saw York, but saw him standing in front of an Indian temple delivering a warm, personal message to Blessed, when all they had heard Eamonn say was that he had merely sent him his best wishes.

When the programme dealt with professionals such problems as those caused by Diana Dors's sons seldom arose. Once they had agreed to contribute a message they were never likely to film one that needed to be tinkered with, even if they really disliked the subject or the programme itself.

When he was asked to say a few words on the 'Life' of BBC

colleague Gloria Hunniford, of whom he could hardly have been said to have been enamoured, disc jockey Jimmy Young showed real 'professionalism'.

For one thing, 'JY' was disappointed when he heard that plans to give him the accolade, instead, had been called off. Even more disappointing for both him and Eamonn because Mrs Thatcher had agreed to appear on it – and that would have been the first time a Prime Minister in office had contributed to a 'This Is Your Life' programme. Young believed the plans were shelved because they were 'leaked' by a national newspaper but, in fact, by then the programme had already been cancelled after researchers had discovered he had a daughter from one of his marriages who did not want to have anything to do with it.

However, he was vital to Gloria Hunniford's programme because her success on radio began when she took over his show as a holiday stand-in. It was no secret at the BBC that afterwards the two of them did not exactly become the closest of friends, and when he was approached about her 'Life' he at first declined to take part.

However, he later changed his mind and millions of viewers – and his amazed colleagues who knew his real feelings about Miss Hunniford – saw him say, with a smile, on the pre-taped message, 'Sorry I wasn't able to make it to my own 'This Is Your Life' but I'm so happy to be on yours. Congratulations. I hope you are enjoying it. Have a great evening. Bye.'

Terry Wogan almost gave the game away – he knew Young's was a less than sincere message. He was waiting behind the scenes to come on right after the film and had to fight to restrain himself from bursting into laughter, as did Miss Hunniford's husband – they were divorced a short time afterwards – who was sitting beside her.

One exception to the rule about professionals was actor Frank Windsor, although circumstances were different in his case because he was the programme's subject not a mere contributor.

The programme team conspired to surprise Windsor, who first became famous on television in the police series 'Z Cars', as he sat down after making an after-dinner speech at a police function, and then to record the rest of the programme in the dining room with the policemen as the audience.

As they sat in an adjoining room with his family and friends, including a Pakistani actor Windsor had once worked with, waiting for him to finish speaking, members of the team realised that the police had been very generous hosts indeed.

Windsor was making jokes in his speech of the kind he apparently thought the majority of his audience wanted to hear, including – as the team sat and squirmed in the presence of the Pakistani actor – some about Commonwealth immigrants.

The only hope for the programme was that the sudden appearance of Eamonn as he sat down at the end of his speech would have a steadying effect on him. It didn't.

If anything it caused a nervous reaction that made him even more boisterous.

And after the horrendous half-hour that followed, the producer ordered nearly twenty edits to be made in the programme before it was transmitted. In part, his instructions to the video-tape editor read:–

* General note: scrub as many reaction shots as possible of subjects.
* Edit out the first shout of 'rubbish'.
* Cut out Dad's gag because of Frank's reaction to it.
* Scrub his 'No' answer when Eamonn asks him if he recognises who is playing cricket with Oscar Naddermier.
* Scrub his 'Who was that?' remark after meeting Gordon Costelow.
* Scrub him saying of Jack Briley: 'You can see he's the only one who's learned his lines.'
* Edit out all his references to 'It's all rehearsed, folks!'
* Edit out his Pakistani send-up and his Pakistani gags.
* Edit out all his shouts of 'rubbish' at the end of the show.

So the policemen who saw the programme being recorded and eagerly sat forward to watch it at their homes a couple of weeks later must have been a very surprised bunch. The programme they saw televised was somewhat different from the after-the-meal-mayhem they witnessed on the night.

Frequently, however, it was not what was taken out but what was artificially inserted that made all the difference to the 'viewability' of 'This Is Your Life'.

The show frequently made 'friends' of comparative strangers.

And if it did not find unknown 'great friends' of the subject at least it found him or her equally unknown 'great admirers', who were usually well-known ratings-getting celebrities.

The device was justified by the argument that, after all, the celebrities *had* heard about the subjects once the programme team had taken the trouble to tell them who they were.

And it nearly always had to be used when the programme went 'on the road', because the selection of subjects was limited to the region where its temporary studio happened to be located.

That was largely because Thames Television claimed grandly that the programme had moved out of London in pursuit of a policy that, whenever possible, it aimed 'to honour local heroes in front of their own people'.

The truth was a little less romantic. In reality Thames had told the production team to go and find somewhere else to make the programme for a week (or two) because it wanted to use its outside broadcast equipment to televise a football match.

Once when they were forced out of London the programme team could only find a studio at Newcastle upon Tyne and reluctantly settled on local born and widely read novelist Catherine Cookson as the subject; reluctantly because she was a very private person with no family and clearly they were going to have tremendous trouble finding enough people to fill the programme, and especially any celebrities to hold the viewers.

But Eamonn had a brainwave. 'Find out which television programmes she watches,' he said.

Back came the information that one was the comedy about wartime soldiering in the Far East, 'It Aint Half Hot Mum', two of the stars of which, Windsor Davies and Melvyn Hayes, just happened to be appearing in pantomime at Newcastle.

It was not difficult – it was a good plug for the pantomime – to persuade them on the programme to say how much they admired her work, too.

By the time the team had also added a nun from California whom she had never before met but had corresponded with, it looked at the end as though the novelist was surrounded by lots of friends – although three of them she had never met in her life before.

But on the 'Life' of John Harris, a wheelchair-bound paraplegic from Pontypool, there were no fewer than four people he had never met.

He was almost as startled to be introduced to former boxing champion and television personality Henry Cooper on the programme as he had been when Eamonn had surprised him with the book moments before.

He was also mystified when Eamonn, told him – and the viewers – that Cooper was a great admirer of his, for he had no idea Henry knew he had become world paraplegic discus-throwing champion two years earlier.

The truth was that Cooper had not even heard of him until the day before the programme when Eamonn had instructed the producer to tell him all about John Harris – and then ask him to appear on his 'This Is Your Life'.

It was his idea of how to brighten up a show – across the script of which he had that morning scrawled in large capitals, 'DULL! DULL! DULL!'

But John Harris's bewilderment did not end with Cooper. No sooner had the programme started than he heard Eamonn say they were going over to the town of Eugene, in Oregon, USA, where two more people he did not know either were going to say how much they admired him. And there on the screen – another of Eamonn's 'strengtheners' – were Richard Slaney and his wife, Mary.

Having been briefed by a researcher, they, too, were able to tell Harris they knew all about his achievements. Though not, of course, for the same reason Cooper did.

But what, if anything, had they to do with his life? Well, said Eamonn, Richard Slaney was a discus thrower, too, and had once been British champion.

And if that was stretching the connection with John a tiny bit, his wife's presence in the show snapped it completely. But, for the ones that count, the millions of viewers, her presence also made it a not-quite-so-dull show.

Because there was a tremendous amount of interest in her just then – as she happened to be Mary Decker, the woman's world mile record-holder, who, not long before, many millions had seen tragically lose her chance of becoming Olympic champion when she was accidentally tripped by Britain's controversial South African-born runner Zola Budd.

That was the real reason she had been asked to film a message in Oregon to a man in London whom she did not know, and whose very existence had only been brought to her attention the day before.

The last guest was Welsh comedian Max Boyce. His connection was stronger than the others, though. He had actually, years before, written a song in praise of the front row forwards who played for Pontypool Rugby Club of which Harris was a supporter!

Ironically, when Boyce himself had been the show's subject a few years earlier, he also found himself shaking hands with somebody he had never seen in his life, a teacher who went on to a tell a story about his schooldays.

Afterwards he tackled the stranger who explained that the teacher who was supposed to be there had to drop out at the last minute. So he had told the programme team he knew the story, too (because his colleague had passed it on to him) and they had accepted his offer to come to London and tell it in his place.

Boyce's presence on that show also brought back to Eamonn not so much a flood but certainly a cascade of unpleasant memories about the comedian's 'This Is Your Life'.

When he was waiting to pounce on him one bitterly cold evening in South Wales, he had to hide behind the Pontypool Rugby Club pavilion to which Boyce was being lured. But Boyce was late and as Eamonn cowered there, getting colder and colder, an ancient member of the club, who had been drinking all afternoon, reeled out of the door, staggered around the back and in the darkness, peed on his foot. Boyce's 'Life', too, had come about because of a 'hit the road' banishment. So did that of Scottish Olympic sprinter Allan Wells which was recorded in Glasgow.

The team soon learned that, following disagreements during the Commonwealth games earlier that year, the local hero was certainly not the idol of his fellow members of the Scottish team, and it was not going to be easy to populate the programme.

Also, Eamonn had scrawled on the first draft of the script a variation of the message he had written on the one for John Harris. This time it said: 'BORING! BORING! BORING!'

So, once again, the team set out to make a subject's 'Life' much more interesting than it really was, starting with the usual first step of asking all his friends and relatives if he had ever had any connection with any famous celebrity. Had he ever met any? Brushed shoulders with any? Been in the same room as any?

Eventually, one of Wells's brothers came up with the name of Muhammad Ali.

Wells didn't exactly know Ali ... hadn't ever actually met him. But in his teens Wells's ambition had been to develop a physique to equal that of the boxer and he had kept a chart of his measurements on his bedroom wall.

Some people may not have thought that this constituted a terribly strong link between the two men, but to the production team, in their desperation to 'glam up' the programme, it practically made Ali Wells's second cousin.

What's more, with Ali's co-operation they could have not one but two contributions from him. One would be the usual 'tribute' – 'from one of the world's greatest athletes to another'. But the other would be even more important. It would consist of an apparently conspiratorial few remarks addressed by Ali, not to the sprinter, but to Eamonn himself. This was to be used at the very start of the programme, even before the 'surprise' was sprung, as a 'tease' to persuade millions of viewers with little interest in athletics to stay tuned long enough to find out what connection the world renowned, larger-than-life character could possibly have with a Scottish sprinter.

And by the time they learned just how tenuous it was, the show would be nearly over but still in the top ten ratings.

Eventually, Ali, who was in Florida training for a series of exhibition bouts, agreed on a payment to film the two pieces and, as always, scripts were written for them.

At least the team would now have a couple of contributions from a recognised international name to brighten up a dull programme.

Or so they thought. Until the film was processed.

Ali's message to Wells was all right. But when the all-important 'curtain raising' message to Eamonn was played back in the editing suite they listened in disbelief.

Ali had kept in only two words of the script – Eamonn's name. And that was only so that he could direct a torrent of abuse directly at him about the time he had been the subject of 'This Is Your Life' himself.

Ali was apparently under the misapprehension the message was intended to be used on a 'Life' *about* Eamonn, and that Eamonn knew in advance as Ali had known about his.

His precise message to Eamonn was: 'Did you know, over here I told them I was going to do a thing for you ... that I'm doing something for Eamonn Andrews? They say "Who he?" Don't even know you! I am going to make you famous in my country, like *I* am in your country, so I want to say I'm glad to be on the show, I'm glad you called me, as you know you still got the same budget, I'm doing this for nothing.

'I'm down here getting ready to box some exhibitions in Saudi Arabia, Pakistan, and India, and somebody told me Eamonn Andrews is having a "This Is Your Life", and I guess that made you feel so good – they are going to give *you* a "This Is Your Life".

'So I says I'll do it, but is it on pay? No, same cheap Eamonn Andrews. So I thank you for letting me be on your show. I hope that you get this; I hope you don't erase none of what I was saying and play all of this so the people can find out how cheap you are!'

So that was it, the team thought, when Ali's attack on Eamonn finally came to an end. All their efforts had finally failed because the American film crew had allowed Ali to ignore the script and let him record what he really wanted to say to Eamonn.

They were about to 'junk' the film before somebody smuggled it to Denis Norden for his programme about television boobs, 'It'll Be All Right On The Night!' when they decided to take one more look at it, this time with the transcript to hand, just in case something was salvageable.

And they found there was. As they went over it again and again they picked out a few words from one sentence, a few from another and had the film edited so that Ali appeared to say them in the order they wanted.

So, when the show was transmitted, millions of viewers heard Eamonn – whom the team had kept in blissful ignorance of what Ali had really said – announce that, before he surprised the person he was after, he was 'going over to Florida' for a brief message from 'legendary boxing champion, Muhammad Ali'.

And viewers heard all that was left of Ali's original message: 'Hello Eamonn Andrews. I'm down here getting ready to box some exhibitions in Saudi Arabia, Pakistan, and India. I want to say I'm glad to be on the show, I'm glad you called me.'

Brief though it was, Eamonn positively glowed as he listened, too.

Skilful editing also spared the blushes of record producer Mickie Most when American rock 'n' roll singer Little Richard, with whom he once appeared on the same bill when he had tried to make a career as a singer was asked to film a message for his 'Life'.

Had they left it exactly as he said it, Most and the viewers, would have heard Little Richard say to him: 'I remember when we toured together. I was top of the bill, you were down at the bottom. You were so bad, they booed you off the stage ... they dragged you off the stage ... sometimes they had to scrape you off the stage. I'm glad to know you made it as a producer. That's where I always knew your future lay. Jesus loves you Mickie.'

The last three sentences were all that were left in for Most – and the viewers – to hear.

Eamonn always insisted that a 'celebrity of international status' was found to add to the 'Life' of every famous British show business personality to whom he presented the book. And if one did not fit in naturally one had to be found who could be 'stitched on' to it.

The reason, he said astutely, was that it flattered the subjects and made them enjoy the programmes more. It did not do any harm to the ratings, either.

But it was not always easy to arrange.

Comedian-writer Eric Sykes had resisted the programme for years, because – he had said – he became superstitious when shortly after Matt (later Sir Matt) Busby, then manager of Manchester United Football Club, had been a subject, the plane carrying the team crashed while attempting to take off at Munich airport and most of the players were killed. In addition several sporting journalists also died and Sir Matt was so critically injured his eventual recovery was considered little less than miraculous.

However, years later, Eric apparently changed his mind – perhaps because by then Sir Matt had been the subject a second time and this had not been followed by a similar catastrophe.

Surrounding Eric with friends from British show business was not difficult but an attempt was made to 'beef up' the programme by adding an international name to the guests.

Perhaps because his comedy is singularly British in flavour, this turned out to be rather difficult.

However, with just a few days to go, his wife recalled that, many years before, Zsa Zsa Gabor had acted in a comedy piece Eric had written.

Well, the programme team told themselves, Zsa Zsa *is* known to audiences on both sides of the Atlantic. So they invited her.

And, what's more, apparently having forgotten her unhappy experience on Eamonn's chat show, she was only too pleased to come.

However, when a researcher met her at London airport he came across one minor complication.

'Welcome to London, Miss Gabor,' he said, as he stepped forward to greet her. 'Thank you for making the journey.'

'Oh, I'm 'appy to oblige, dollink,' said Miss Gabor. 'But by the way, oo is this Shykes?'

She had no recollection of having heard of Eric, let alone meet him. So before the programme photographs of 'this Shykes' were sent around to her hotel for her to study to ensure that when she walked on into the glare of the studio lights she did not launch herself on to Eamonn by mistake.

When she did make her big entrance and gave him her effusive greeting, Eric returned it with equal ardour.

But then he was only behaving as all professionals do on such occasions. That so-called professionalism, which enables experienced show business people never to look discomfited once they are 'working', no matter what, has perhaps been the production team's greatest ally.

Especially when the pros were comedians. They were the ones on whom the show depended to inject a little fun and laughter into many an otherwise lifeless line-up. Or simply make up the numbers of 'pals'.

Comedian Ken Dodd was quite candid when he agreed – yet again – to film a contribution to the 'Life' of a comedian less successful than himself. He said to the researcher, 'When you ask me to be on the show I know the person you're doing hasn't got many friends.'

That was sadly very true. In earlier days a person so isolated would simply have been ruled out as too high on the 'boredom scale' to be considered as a subject.

But in the fourth decade of its existence the shortage was so acute that the programme could not afford to ignore any possible subject no matter how uneventful his or her life had been.

The trouble was that to make such shows 'stand up' as pieces of entertainment more and more bizarre devices were being invented.

And many of them were to prove to be very much more questionable than merely asking a comedian to pretend he was a friend.

16

A stage packed
with people – but 'Life's'
an empty book

Eamonn was certainly right about his policy of 'friend faking' because few of the subjects ever protested.

There were, however, many complaints from subjects afterwards about guests they had expected but, for one reason or another, had been omitted.

After her 'Life' news reader and quiz show hostess Angela Rippon listed a number of people she said should have been on (not knowing most of them had been approached and declined) and even complained that her dogs and cats had not been included. She referred to those members of her menagerie because one of the parts of the programme she had most enjoyed had been a piece of film of her horse.

But she may not have been so pleased had she known how her horse, and those on the 'Life' programmes of actress Liza Goddard and comedian Ted Rogers among others, was made to appear to 'talk' to her on the film to get an audience laugh.

The trick was that mustard powder was rubbed on the horses' top lip – it was the contortions they made trying to get the stinging stuff off that caused them to twitch their lips and move their tongues as though articulating the words spoken by the voice that had been dubbed on the film.

Former British and American Open Golf Champion, Henry Cotton, who was in his eighty-second year when his 'Life' was produced, was another who was very candid in his reaction to it.

Looking round the hospitality room afterwards at the people who had been had brought on to 'honour' him, he said to Eamonn in a very loud voice, 'Your lot must have had an interesting time digging up all these half-dead people.'

Eamonn also got many a surprise – besides the two absolute refusals – when he went to spring his surprise.

When he halted the open-topped car comedy actor Bernard Cribbins was driving into a West End side street at the time, and showed him the book, Cribbins grabbed it from his hand and said, 'Thank you very much, I'll read it later.'

Then, as Eamonn stood dumbfounded, he put it on the seat beside him and drove off with it.

Fortunately the road further along was blocked by stationary traffic and when Cribbins had to stop again, he returned the book to a panicking, perspiring Eamonn who had chased after him.

And when Eamonn thrust the book at war hero Lord Lovat in another London street, as he was on his way to what he thought was to be an interview about his own book 'March Past', the commando leader, who did not recognise him, said politely, 'Oh thank you – is this for me?'

Then, without checking his step, he swept the book from Eamonn's hand, and marched off with it tucked under his arm like a Field Marshal's baton. Eamonn had to run after him to get it back and explain who he was and exactly what was supposed to be happening.

That was not the only time he suffered the indignity of not being recognised when he least expected it, however. When he walked on to the set where all the guests were assembled for a rehearsal of the 'Life' of Susannah York, the actress's sister, Mrs Carolyn Cunningham-Brown, pointed in his direction and in a voice loud enough for everybody to hear, including Eamonn, asked, 'Who's that? What does he do?'

And much less polite than Lord Lovat's response to Eamonn's challenge was that of Liverpool docker-turned-sculptor Arthur Dooley. Eamonn surprised him outside the House of Commons, where the then Prime Minister, Harold Wilson (later Lord Wilson), had arranged for him to hold an exhibition.

Said Eamonn, smiling confidently for the benefit of the cameras and the small crowd of onlookers, 'I know why *you're* here, Arthur. Do you know why *I'm* here?'

'Do I fuck!' replied Dooley.

Bolstering a show with three or four celebrities the subject had never met, as in the cases of Catherine Cookson and John Harris, was one thing, but in a real emergency when the complement on the set was really going to look sparse, and the subject decidedly lonely, it was a case of send for the cavalcade.

The cavalcade was a very useful device. It was used to fill up the studio with people and add a few interesting faces to the programme while also giving the impression the subject had lots and lots of friends.

In fact, he or she probably had never even met most of the mob who suddenly came rushing on with a handshake.

Sometimes, as with the bizarre cavalcade that swelled the 'Life' of actor Harry Andrews, the connection was totally spurious.

The 'Life' on Andrews came about as an expediency different from the more usual geographical one. Originally he was to be a contributor on one of Michael Winner who had been chosen not for himself but for the ratings-pulling big Hollywood names Eamonn hoped would come on the programme for such a successful film director.

In fact, researchers were not even able to find enough people who were friends of his to make a 'Life' programme on Winner at all.

So they abandoned the idea, plucked Andrews from its proposed 'guest list', and hurriedly started getting together a 'This Is Your Life' on him instead.

But they soon discovered they had landed themselves in exactly the same problem they thought they had just escaped from.

Andrews who had never married and whose only close family was one surviving sister, was a very private man who had very few associates and soon they were again struggling to assemble sufficient people.

By then, however, the team had to stay with him or lose the studio date altogether and be without a single show ready for transmission (a constant threat that led them to make many 'Lives' they would not otherwise have contemplated).

How they swelled the ranks for the Harry Andrews programme

was another of Eamonn's brainwaves.

The 'hit' was to be made when, steered there by his agent, the veteran actor was walking past the site of the now demolished theatre where he had made his West End debut fifty years before.

That was the source of Eamonn's inspiration. 'Let's have a cavalcade of people who are appearing in the West End *right now*', he suggested. 'A salute to somebody who started there half-a-century ago from those whose names are there in lights today.'

At such short notice it was not easy to persuade 'star names' to co-operate. So waiting at the spot 'to greet him' – and whom Andrews totally ignored – was a motley collection of sixteen actors, none of whom he had ever met, only half a dozen of whom the team themselves had even heard of, and few of whom merited even a 25 watt bulb. All were, understandably, quite happy to be seen on television and get a plug for the show in which they were appearing at the same time.

Andrews was, of course, one of those who made it quite clear to Eamonn at the 'pick-up' that he hated the whole thing.

And it was a bemused subject who, on the show, was asked to meet 'those stars of the West End's Theatreland who arranged that 50th anniversary surprise for you tonight.'

That, of course, was totally untrue. But the thinking behind it helped fill the stage.

As did the cavalcade of nurses on Joan Collins's 'Life', the cavalcade of former international goalkeepers for England 'keeper, Peter Shilton, and the cavalcade of former Ryder Cup players for golfer-turned-commentator, Peter Allis.

Numerically, though, none equalled the bizarre cavalcade recruited for the 'Life' of a pop-music person named Bernard William Jewry.

The programme sent out an open invitation to pop people of the Sixties, when Jewry had been known as Shane Fenton – and the Seventies and Eighties, when he became Alvin Stardust.

What hit them was not a cavalcade but an avalanche.

Before they knew what was happening, forty-six assorted pop people of varying degrees of notability had arrived at the studio. Eamonn could not possibly get all their names in the right order. It did not matter though. Stardust did not know most of them anyway.

However, for total non-connection none surpassed the cavalcade for Derek Jameson which consisted of a dozen about-to-be BBC disc-jockey 'colleagues'. All were there at the programme's request and after much arm-twisting by the BBC, who wanted to give the impression there was no internal resentment at his appointment.

It was not only on the programme that the team experienced cavalcades. Regularly they had to go through a cavalcade of would-be subjects before they even found somebody to have a cavalcade for in the first place.

The search to find just one viable programme in the month preceding the Jameson show started with Olympic showjumper Lucinda Prior Palmer.

But her mother had just booked a cruise and had no intention of changing it.

The next was comedy actor Bernard Bresslaw, considered to be 'right' because he was appearing in a comedy in the West End. But research revealed there was little to laugh at in his life just then. In the previous six months there had been no fewer than four bereavements in his family.

International goalkeeper Peter Shilton, who had just been made an MBE, went into the frame. But his team, Southampton, was about to play a cup match and if it was drawn the replay would be on the same day as the programme.

Number four was Richard Vernon. But it was not the rather serious mannered actor himself who was the attraction, it was somebody appearing with him in a West End comedy – David Jason, 'Del Boy' of the television hit, 'Only Fools and Horses'.

Jason had made it very clear he would run a mile if Eamonn came after him, personally, but the team reckoned viewers would stay switched on for him if he was in at the start of Vernon's 'Life'.

However, researchers were told that the play was about to close and they would not be able to have an 'on-stage' 'pick-up' with Vernon and Jason. So down came Vernon's name and they started to look for candidate number five.

Eventually, they decided to go for Michael Elphick, who was having great success in the television series, 'Boon'.

But it turned out that he, too, had made it clear that he would have nothing to do with the programme.

Close to despair (again it was not an unfamiliar emotion) they learned that the information that the Jason comedy was closing had been wrong.

So up went Vernon's name again. And when Eamonn made the hit there was 'Del Boy' obligingly at his side.

At the end of the programme Vernon got a 'This Is Your Life' book – and Michael Elphick joined David Jason, and a couple of hundred more, in the programme's 'hate book'. That was a large ledger in which were logged the names of the celebrities who had given instructions to their agents, wives or husbands, that Eamonn must never be allowed to approach them, and why.

Wisely it was kept secret from Eamonn, himself, because the most often stated reason was: 'Does not like Eamonn or the programme'.

It was not unusual for subjects to be chosen, as Richard Vernon was, not for themselves, but for the other guests they brought to the show.

Photographer Terry O'Neil was chosen because his then wife Faye Dunaway, from whom he was, of course, shortly to be divorced, happened to be a Hollywood 'star' who had agreed to appear with Eamonn at the very start of the show, even before the 'pick-up' in fact, and whose presence was expected to hold the viewers throughout the entire programme.

And Michael Winner's proposed 'Life' was not the only one in which a would-be guest became the subject instead.

Youthful musical 'star' Bonnie Langford was to have been a guest on the 'Life' of singer Lena Zavoroni when those plans were shelved because her parents decided to split up too close to the proposed taping date. However, as the two young ladies had spent so much of their lives together and had so many mutual friends, out went Zavornoi and in went Langford.

And, as Eric Morecambe used to say, nobody could see the join.

When it came to doctoring a 'This Is Your Life' script, Eamonn's long experience of course, made him an expert at hiding anything he did not want viewers to see.

Sometimes it happened to be the truth he decided to hide.

Particularly if he thought it was going to prevent a programme from including the ingredient which more than any other was the cause of its phenomenal success, the emotion engendered by the renowned family reunions it so frequently effected.

Or appeared to effect.

Because sometimes they were not the heart-touching, bringing together of relatives and friends who had not seen each other for many years – and, but for 'This Is Your Life', would never have met again – they seemed to be.

Sometimes they were quite cynically invented.

Manufacturing them was a technique itself and Eamonn was an expert. The method was, however, fairly simple. He would remind the subject that certain friends or relatives had gone to live in a faraway country many years before and it was to some obscure part of that country that the programme had traced them and flown them all the way to London ... 'especially to be with you tonight'.

But if researchers had discovered the irritating, spoilsport fact that those friends or relatives had kept in close touch over the years and visited one another many times Eamonn simply struck those details from the script.

Instead he would mention where the friend or relative was living and then insert a phrase such as ' ... and it was there that we found her (or him).' By this, and further elaborations about how far away the place was and how many miles the programme had flown the relative, he managed to give the impression that a 'reunion' had only been made possible by the expensive and painstaking, earth-scouring detective work of his researchers. Neglecting to mention that the only earth-scouring necessary had been just one long-distance phone call.

As well as hiding facts the programme did not want subjects and viewers to know, it also had ways of persuading them they had seen things they had not.

If, early in the programme, they saw those 'long lost' relatives pop up to send their greetings on a piece of film clearly shot in the distant part of the world where researchers had 'found' them, the subject and viewers could be lulled into believing they were still there. So, when they came walking on at the programme's end the surprise and emotion were heightened very much more and tears flowed in torrents.

However, to send a crew all that way to work the trick was usually prohibitively expensive.

So those touching messages from afar were frequently filmed *after* the relatives had arrived in London, usually only a couple of hours before the programme had started and very often even in the very same studio – while they were standing in front of a backdrop of Sydney Harbour bridge, or the New York skyline, or some other scene that suggested the film had been shot thousands of miles away.

Despite the fact that they were occasionally sceptical about the programme's claims, not only viewers but newspapers were sometimes taken in by Eamonn's practised word juggling.

During the programme on former Newcastle United and England footballer, Jackie Milburn, an aunt was brought on who had given him a home after he had absconded from his lowly kitchen job in an affluent London household where he had been sent as a youngster.

Later the aunt had gone to live in the United States but Milburn had always kept in touch and had visited her. But that fact was omitted and after he had brought her on to the programme a national newspaper congratulated Eamonn and his team on finding the aunt and reuniting Milburn with her 'after more than thirty years'.

A similar emotional peak seemed to have been reached when on the 'Life' of comedian Ted Rogers Eamonn mentioned a great pal from his days as a National Serviceman in the Royal Air Force.

He went on, 'He went to work in America when his service days ended, thirty years ago. But from North Carolina to be reunited with you tonight, your closest pal from those RAF days ...'

As the friend then came on to a mutual warm embrace, viewers thought they were again seeing two people who, thanks to Eamonn and the programme, were meeting for the first time in thirty years.

What Eamonn had not said was that the comedian's friend visited Britain and contacted him frequently, and their last meeting had only been a short time before the programme.

A more sustained example of Eamonn's technique came in the 'life' of another comedian Stan Stennett, who at the time was also one of the stars of the long-running 'soap opera', 'Crossroads'.

As so frequently happened, researchers found some facts about Stennett's life they did not expect. They discovered he had been born out of wedlock in a Welsh mining community, but that his mother subsequently married and later gave birth to two more sons.

Although one of those two half-brothers was subsequently adopted and taken to live in Australia, Stennett always kept in close touch with both of them.

The line that was to introduce the younger of the two on to his 'Life' originally read, 'He was adopted and went with his parents to live in Australia when he was only twelve, thirty-five years ago, though you have kept in touch since. But we have flown him from his home in New South Wales ...'

That may have been the truth but it was far from emotional enough for Eamonn. He decided he would say, 'He went to Australia thirty-five years ago but we have managed to trace him to the small town where he now lives.'

On that particular 'This Is Your Life' there happened to be a director new to the programme who dared challenge Eamonn for manipulating the words to give what he considered to be a false impression.

Eventually Eamonn, who was somewhat taken aback by this boldness, condescended not to claim the programme had found the brother in Australia and brought him back for a reunion. But then he went on triumphantly to declare that, instead, he would say a still emotionally charged line, 'He went to live in Australia thirty years ago. But for you, tonight, he's home again – at last!'

Then, gleefully, he yelled at the bewildered director, 'I defy you to find a lie in that! In fact, I defy you to find even half a lie!' The director did not bother to take up the challenge.

The finale of that programme reminded me of the response the wife of former Liberal leader Jo Grimond (later Lord Grimond) made when she was approached and asked if she would agree to a 'This Is Your Life' on him.

'I'd be delighted to assist,' she said. Then, in an amusingly accurate reflection of the average person's view of the programme, she added, 'But tell me. Is it *compulsory* for someone from Australia to come on at the end?'

The many millions of his admirers and regular viewers of the two most important programmes in his career, 'This Is Your Life' and 'What's My Line?' were all too willing to believe Eamonn really did glow with that 'transparent honesty' with which he was credited at the time of his death. It would seem to have been essential to his stewardship of both shows.

In fact, besides squeezing extra tears from, and adding extra glitter to 'This Is Your Life' by these methods, he also, encouraged the rules of 'What's My Line?' to be bent, if not broken, in the belief that it would make the programme more entertaining and therefore more successful.

But perhaps the greatest deception he ever perpetrated – because it took in both the viewers and the subjects for more than thirty years – was the 'This Is Your Life' book itself. When Eamonn thrust it in front of the chosen person and announced 'This Is Your Life', then protectively took it away again as though to prevent any premature peeping, everybody thought it was all there between those bright red covers. But there was no life story in that book at all. In fact, there was not a single word in it. Every page was completely blank.

While Eamonn was surprising somebody with that dummy book – or occasionally their reactions to it were suprising him – a scriptwriter, a script secretary, a production assistant, and a researcher or two, were still making the changes he kept demanding until there was no time left in which to make them.

Then, at the last minute, the script was stuck inside the covers of the 'programme book' which was identical to the phoney 'pick-up book'.

That was the book Eamonn used throughout the shows and presented to the subjects with great ceremony as the programmes ended.

But they were not allowed to keep that book either or even take a squint inside it, because it was full of deletions and insertions and scrawled amendments.

When the cameras were switched off it too was taken from them.

Weeks, maybe months, later, and often after they had had to pester the programme, a third book, this time containing a set of still photographs taken during the show, was sent to them.

Meantime, the 'book' which Eamonn had first shown to the subject, had been put back on the shelf – after the adhesive strip on which the name of the 'guest of honour' was printed in gold had been ripped from it.

The following week ... and the week after ... and the week after that ... it was taken out of the cupboard again. On the front was stuck the name of yet another subject who blithely believed his life story was contained within its covers and he was the only person who ever lived to whom that particular book in Eamonn's hand had ever been dedicated.

It was all part of the great illusion, like the stitched-on celebrities, the friend-faking, the doctored films, the tributes that were tagged on afterwards, the reunions that never were.

At one script meeting in the year before he died, Eamonn said wearily but with unusual frankness, 'The trouble with this programme is that sometimes we can't remember what's true and what's been made up.'

He said it in a tone that suggested everybody but himself was to blame, because of all the people he deceived he deceived himself more than anybody.

For at the very start of his career he had clearly accepted that the only way to survive the competition in television was to go along with the slogan reputedly invented by the public relations profession, 'There are no such things as lies, just expedient exaggerations.'

He practised this so often that over the years he began to believe that not to be challenged in a lie was the same as telling the truth.

Normally he restricted his habit of trotting out those untruths to when the cameras were switched on. But once he did it just after they had been switched off and it immediately rebounded on him.

The choice of Stan Stennett as subject had been another one of expediency when the programme had been obliged to vacate its London studio temporarily and find facilities elsewhere.

In his case the studio it found was at Bristol just across the Bristol Channel from South Wales, where he was born. Consequently there were a lot of his Welsh friends in the audience and when the programme finished they began to sing the country's unofficial anthem, 'We'll Keep A Welcome In The Hillside'.

So Eamonn decided to milk the emotion by telling a fib in his thank you speech to the audience after the show, too. 'I'm so glad we made the decision to travel *specially to Bristol* so that I could tell the life story of this great Welshman right here in his own country,' he told them with all the sincerity he could muster.

Whereupon a local man in the audience yelled out, 'Bristol's in England, you berk.'

Although Eamonn frequently said things that were not quite true, that was the only time, as far as the members of his production team were aware, that he did not even know what country he was in when he was saying them.

17

Back to the 'Line'
– but it isn't
quite straight

By 1984 Eamonn was finally persuaded that to fulfil the two-programme contract he had always insisted on, in the hope that it would prompt Thames to find a new programme for him that would supersede the bewhiskered 'This Is Your Life', he would again have to turn back the clock. In fact, turn it back even further, to the very start of his television career, and bring back a programme which had started in Britain even before 'This Is Your Life'. He agreed to be question master of a revival of 'What's My Line?' which he had first chaired at the BBC thirty-three years before.

The 1984 version differed in what appeared to the viewer to be one minor detail but there was in fact a very significant reason for it. The change was that the 'traditional' panel of four was increased to five.

It was made only days before the first of the new series of 'What's My Line?' was to be televised, to bring onto the panel the exceedingly popular comedian Eric Morecambe whose role would be to make use of a specially designed questioning technique that would guarantee the old programme would at least generate a lot of laughter.

The producers of the American 'What's My Line?' who had devised the technique argued that it was not an infraction of the rules, although many people might have disagreed.

Eamonn, who had come across it during his guest appearances

on the American show had no qualms about promoting its use as a ratings weapon for the revived programme.

But, ironically, the ambivalent attitude he was later to take towards it was to be the first step to a situation in which some of the panellists were soon cheating quite outrageously.

The stance Eamonn took was that he wanted the technique to succeed as long as implementing it did not usurp the week-by-week decisions he made on the 'shape' of the show. In other words Eric Morecambe could have his laughs just as long as Eamonn could continue with his career-long compulsion for making changes in a show until there was absolutely no time left in which to make any more.

Members of Thames management were delighted Eric Morecambe had agreed to become a panellist. They were badly missing the tremendously popular comedy spectaculars he used to make for them with his partner, Ernie Wise, but was no longer able to for health reasons. The ratings boost he could give the veteran quiz show would be at least some consolation.

They were also hoping he would agree to make many more appearances than the initial three to which he had agreed. By then he would know if he had been right to risk his professional reputation late in his career on a type of programme of which he had no experience whatsoever.

There was reason for optimism. The technique by which Eric was to try to get laughs had been a large contributory factor to the initial success of the original American 'What's My Line?' And that success had been phenomenal.

Pallid though it might seem by comparison with present-day quiz programmes that pander to greed, it ran for twenty-five years from the beginning of the Fifties and was the longest running game show ever.

The American producers realised immediately the first show was made that if a panellist 'personalised' a certain kind of question it would always get a laugh.

From then on they were not prepared to leave those laughs to chance. They devised a method – by which a funnyman panellist would be given certain questions to ask – to make sure they came on every show.

It helped if there was something slightly 'naughty' about the challenger's job description. So if a contestant made an article of ladies' underwear a comic on the panel would be 'programmed' first to establish the job had to do with an article of clothing (nothing suspicious about that), then ask the challenger if he, the panellist, would wear it himself.

The mental picture of a famous male celebrity putting on an article of ladies lingerie would get a laugh from the studio audience. And – however unlikely it might be (though not in every case) – the quiz master could truthfully answer the question about the panellist wearing it, 'Yes, if you wanted to.'

So, as the rules permitted him to keep asking until he got a 'no' answer, the panellist still kept the questionning. He would continue with similarly prepared questions aimed at more laughs ... 'Would I wear it in the house? ... in the bedroom? ... on my head?'

The American producers called the technique 'gambiting'. Other people might have used a more prosaic word – cheating.

When I discussed it with Eamonn, after I had been asked to supply 'gambiting' questions to Eric Morecambe, he told me that while he was 'guesting' in the States he had learned that comedian Steve Allen, one of the most successful panellists on the American show, had all his questions written for him by his own writers.

And he added that as, in order to prepare the questions, the writers obviously needed to know the answers in advance there was no doubt Allen knew them, too.

However, when I asked if he was implying Eric Morecambe should also be given the answers, he was evasive and enigmatic. 'All I *will* say is, if the show is going to succeed the panellists are going to need all the help they can get,' he said. 'In my experience viewers don't watch losing teams. And you can make what you like of that.'

Then he added a remark which was so familiar his backroom teams had been mimicking it for nearly forty years, 'Whatever you do, I don't want to know a *single* thing about it.'

This, of course, was his insurance that if it was ever put to him he would always be able to say with complete conviction that he had no *certain* knowledge of anything untoward happening behind the scenes on any of his shows.

The so-called gambiting was a technique that could, of course, only be used to its best advantage by comedians, and intelligent comedians at that. Eric Morecambe was perfect for it.

At first it seemed applying it would be fairly straightforward. After I had learned the occupations of the challengers chosen for the first programme I worked out sets of 'gambiting' questions for each one. These I numbered from one to four to correspond with the order in which they would be brought on, then phoned Eric.

Eric himself did not have a single misgiving about these tactics. 'I bet those American panellists knew plenty,' he said, accurately. 'And why not? After all, it's only a game. There aren't any five pound notes wrapped up in the certificates the winners get.'

He, too, had heard that Steve Allen's writers had devised his questions. 'It only makes sense,' he said. 'The important thing is to make the programme funny.' There were still a few days to go when I phoned him – plenty of time for him to memorise the questions and the order in which to ask them.

But then Eamonn took a hand and with just minutes before that first show was to go on the air the whole plan suddenly fell apart. To my astonishment, I discovered that, because in his view it would 'improve the programme's balance', Eamonn had ordered that the last two challengers be switched around so that original challenger number three became number four, and number four came on in the third spot. And, in his usual dismissive manner, he refused even to discuss it further.

This late switch, of course, threatened disaster for Eric's debut as a quiz show panellist and because of his policy of playing the ostrich I could not intervene with Eamonn personally. Besides, I knew it would not make any difference. Eamonn made such decisions, capricious though they often may have seemed, because he genuinely considered them to be very important. By that he meant important to his own performance. He never seemed to think it mattered if they had the very opposite effect on anybody else's.

And his decisions that day were going to have a detrimental effect on Eric's performance in not many minutes time unless I could do something about it. Because of Eamonn's switch he now had the wrong questions for the wrong contestants and if he asked them in the order I had given they would simply sound nonsensical.

The only way to prevent that was somehow to let him know about Eamonn's switch without being overheard in the show's crowded hospitality room.

When I went in Eric was sitting in a corner, looking very gloomy and deep in thought, no doubt going over the prepared questions in his mind. As I approached I mouthed the message that I had some urgent information.

Suddenly, behind those famous heavy rimmed glasses, that look of gloom turned to one of panic as his instincts told him something had gone wrong with the live show just minutes away.

Pretending to study something on the wall, I managed to whisper the message that two of the contestants had been switched. Then I sat down beside him and we carried on a conversation like a pair of ventriloquists, desperately trying not to let anybody see our lips moving. If anybody had overheard us it would have sounded somewhat mysterious.

'Oh, thod it!' Eric hissed. 'Gich gones, for God thake? 'umber gone and 'umber two?'

'No,' I breathed, through clenched teeth, ''umber free's now 'umber four'

'So the last gone's 'umber free?'

'Thath right.'

'Oh, gollocks!'

It was with his mind in that muddle that Eric Morecambe faced live television cameras for one of the very few times in his memorable career.

He got out a couple of standard opening questions to the first challenger, a busty, blonde lady wrestler: 'Do you provide a service? ... Could I avail myself of that service?'

But, because of the pre-programme panic, he completely forgot the 'gambiting' questions with which he should have continued: 'Could I do what you do? ... Could I do it with you? ... Would I enjoy it? ... Would you enjoy it?', and so on.

Not exactly cerebral stuff but they would have got him a few encouraging giggles.

But, had he even managed to bring the questions to mind, he did not get the chance to put them to the challenger anyway. Her occupation was guessed before the questioning came around to him again.

Eric managed to put just two questions to the next contestant, a spot from which we did not expect many laughs anyway, and then came the 'Mystery Guest' – whose identity the panel had to try to guess while blindfolded – heavyweight boxer Frank Bruno.

This was the one spot for which I had not given him a prepared line of questions. It was a totally phoney spot, anyway, because Eamonn wanted the 'celebrity' to be identified as soon as seemed decent, to allow him as much time as possible for the interview that followed.

He decreed that even with their attempts at false voices and with the panellists' sight impeded by the masks (which were really more decorative than effective, I found) celebrities really believed themselves to be so much larger than life that their egos would be badly bruised if they were not identified fairly promptly.

Eamonn spent so long talking boxing to Bruno, partly because of the rarity of feeling so much at ease with the subject under discussion, there was only time for one of the two remaining challengers.

Eric got a 'no' to the second question he put to a two-man team of 'bird scarers' – their job was to frighten birds away from jet planes preparing to take off from London airport and we had hoped he would get a few laughs from their job description. That was his final contribution to the programme. By then he had no idea which questions he was supposed to ask of whom.

So, by his standards, and thanks to Eamonn's intervention, he considered his performance a fiasco.

After the show Eamonn, sensibly protecting himself, refused to be drawn into any discussion about how his late changes had affected Eric's 'gambiting'. Clearly there was little point in providing Eric with a special set of questions for any future show.

But how to make him happy enough to stay with it?

To have any hope of repairing his tattered confidence he needed a 'crutch' he knew Eamonn could not kick from under him (whether by accident or otherwise).

The simple solution would have been to throw away the rules altogether and tell him all the answers in advance. But it was felt that might be too drastic a measure, at this stage at any rate. Instead it was decided to give him 'hints' about the contestants' occupations, stopping just short of the actual occupations themselves.

At the very least, that meant Eric would then be able to prepare some intelligent sounding questions. Free of the constraint of worrying about his mind going blank – the so-called 'goldfish syndrome' when the panellist's mouth opens and closes but little more than a grunt comes out – he would be able to concentrate on putting some humour into his performance.

On the next show-day two programmes were to be made 'back-to-back', one to be transmitted live, the other to be recorded for transmission the following week. The second of them would complete the 'trial period' to which Eric had agreed.

So, as soon as I had the two sets of contestants I phoned him and gave him a one line clue to each one's occupation.

Late in the afternoon of the day of the show I learned that Eamonn had *again* switched contestants around.

But this time we were much less worried. Eric had to make a mental switch with two one-line clues rather than whole sets of questions. He was much happier with his performances and afterwards was much better disposed towards returning a couple of months later.

But, tragically, four weeks afterwards he collapsed and died while making a brief guest appearance in a concert at a friend's theatre.

By then, however, the amount of 'fixing' that had gone on had now made the programme farcical.

When Ernie Wise had come in to replace Eric after those first three shows, no attempt was made to introduce him to 'gambiting'. Instead, he was immediately given the kind of help his partner had ultimately received.

However, despite the improvement brought by Eric's funnier performance, critics had described the show as 'creaking' and the panel as 'The Feeble Five'.

So, in an effort to speed up the game, the practice of giving clues to the answers had been extended to other regular panellists, Barbara Kelly who had been on the original BBC version, writer Jilly Cooper, actor Patrick Mower and politician and novelist Jeffrey Archer.

It had been decided unwise to include journalist George Gale because he might feel misleading the viewers in this way was sufficiently reprehensible for him to refuse to join in and instead expose the practice in his newspaper column.

Now matters began to escalate even further. Patrick Mower had none of the qualms it was feared George Gale might have had. He had suspected from the start that Eric Morecambe was 'being shown favouritism' and that so, too, was Ernie Wise, and as soon as he was given clues to the answers he asked straight out to be given the answers themselves.

He pleaded that he had just opened in a play in the West End and it was tough enough remembering his lines without trying to fathom out the meaning of the clues.

He also argued that if he did not have to worry about trying to guess the answers he would be able to put in a *performance* on the show. 'I'm sure that's *really* what Thames Television want of me,' he said.

When they were still not forthcoming, he said he would promise he would seldom, if ever, come out with the right answers. 'Most of the time I'll pretend to be completely baffled,' he said. 'I can fake that. I'm an actor. It's what I do best.'

I happened to be the member of the team who listened to all that. Quite suddenly the whole thing seemed quite ridiculous and, compared with the original challenge of trying to get laughs for a very funny man like Eric Morecambe, a totally unedifying experience. I cut the whole thing short by giving Mower the answers he asked for.

When he had first asked for them Mower had insisted it was not because he wanted to look clever. Not long afterwards Jeffrey Archer was making a similar plea – but he was saying, frankly, that it was because he *did* want to look clever.

I was in the hospitality room when Archer, then soon to become deputy chairman of the Conservative Party (until he resigned because of the newspaper call girl allegations which led to his successful libel action), openly asked me to go with him to his dressing room for a word in private.

In the atmosphere of that kind of show where panellists, and not forgetting their agents and friends, are constantly suspicious and on the look-out to see if anybody is getting any pointers they are not (one 'What's My Line?' panellist claimed she had never been on *any* quiz-show without getting some advance help) such a request made publicly was, I felt, somewhat indiscreet. But to have refused would have drawn even more attention to it. So, watched by every eye in the room, I followed Archer out.

Once out of earshot of the others, Archer went straight into an odd entreaty about how on the previous week's programme he had concentrated so much on the clues he had been given that he had not been able to take in the answers other panellists were getting. 'Frankly it was very confusing,' he said.

Obviously, the simplest way to stop the clues causing him confusion was not to give him any in the first place. But he went on to say, 'If you were to give me the answers instead I would be able to make up some interesting questions. I promise you, that's what I would like to do, not come out with all the right answers on the programme. When I have asked my questions I can send the questioning on to the next panellist who then might get the right answer, not me.'

Clearly, the longer we were in the dressing room the more suspicious the other panellists would become. Equally clearly, the quickest way out was to give him the answers. That's what I did. The quite ridiculous proportions the whole thing had now reached helped me make the decision without too much conscience searching.

After that, to make sure there would be no similarly embarrassing encounters, the answers were conveyed by telephone. During the second phone conversation he gave me a candid explanation of why he wanted all this privileged information. 'I like to have the answers because it makes me seem clever,' he said, 'And I like to look clever, thank you very much.'

The 'Mystery Guest' spot was a farce in its own right. Although steps were taken to ensure their identities were *not* a total mystery, the celebrities themselves were not in the conspiracy. Knowing that panellists were told who they were in advance as a precaution against them not being able to identify them, or taking too long about it, would not have helped their egos either. Nor did the programme team want to put a strain on their often not very brilliant acting talents.

So, to keep the whole business convincing, their drivers were instructed to take them to an entrance different from the one used by the panellists. Then, with an elaborate show of secrecy, they were taken by a roundabout route to their dressing rooms, where they were asked to stay out of sight until the panellists were safely in the studio for the start of the programme.

Whether the contestants were celebrities ('slebs') or 'civilians', as non-slebs are called in television, the production team marvelled week after week at the Oscar-worthy performances with which some panellists disguised the fact that they had been given the answers, or very little short of the answers, in advance.

Parlaying the audience, as it was called, was the most common method used to get to the answer without causing suspicion. To do this, the panellists made an apparently accidental remark that was greeted by audience laughter or applause.

Then they 'realised' the audience's response meant the 'chance remark' was a clue and, apparently demonstrating amazing powers of deduction, they pretended to follow that clue to a triumphant conclusion and more applause.

Being supplied with clues to the answers certainly came as no surprise to one seasoned panellist who, on receipt of them, simply shrugged and declared, 'I've been given the same sort of help on *every* quiz programme on which I have ever appeared.'

Not surprisingly, all the pre-programme information made the panel very much a winning team. And very soon it was winning so often there was a danger too much suspicion would be aroused – although not by the companies' 'watchog', the Independent Broadcasting Authority, which was considered to be even more blind than the panel was supposed to be during the mystery guest spot.

At one point, when not a single challenger had won in a month, newspapers started to comment about the panel's repeated success. So those panellists who were in the know were asked not to be too clever too often.

By then newspaper critics were saying such things as, 'Somebody should tell Ernie Wise to slow down a bit. He's guessing the challengers' lines so quickly they'll soon run out of contestants.' Or, 'Is it sacrilege to suggest that they have been given a script?'

Little did they know how right they were.

And little could they know how right Eamonn had been been – in his determination to make the venerable old programme succeed in the Eighties – to suggest the panellists should be given all the help possible.

Because, with that help, 'The Feeble Five' had by then lifted Eamonn and his 'creaking' show to the upper reaches of the ratings – which seemed to confirm Eamonn's remark that, like football fans, when it comes to panel games television viewers only want to watch a winning team.

However it was achieved and whatever the critics said, lightheartedly or otherwise, to be up there at the top of the ratings charts meant Eamonn was a success. And it was a place with which he had become very familiar during his career and somewhere he believed he belonged until the very end of it.

Fade-out . . .

On the morning of the last day of October, 1987, a Saturday, Eamonn sat down at the desk in the study of his London flat and wrote a note for his secretary of many years to read when she came in on the following Monday.

It was to remind her to order thirty-six red roses for Eamonn to present to Grainne on their thirty-sixth wedding anniversary exactly one week later.

She scarcely needed reminding, however. Eamonn had bought Grainne red roses for their anniversary every year for twenty-five years, ever since their eleventh anniversary when, as he was about to leave Broadcasting House late in the evening, he remembered he had not bought her a present at all.

A BBC colleague had come to the rescue by suggesting he buy eleven roses and write a note telling Grainne he had bought one short of a dozen, not only because that was the number of married years they were celebrating, but because the twelfth rose was herself.

Very much taken by the idea, Eamon had bought the roses from a flower seller in Regent Street. When she told him they were £3 he gave her a fiver thinking she meant £3 for the lot. But Grainne had been so delighted he quickly got over the shock of finding out they were £3 each and had continued to buy her red roses on every wedding anniversary since.

Sadly, however, Eamonn did not live to give her those roses for their thirty-sixth anniversary. Instead, just ten days later, they were lovingly laid on his coffin when he was buried at Balgriffin cemetery, close to the family home near Dublin.

He had felt very tired that Saturday morning; more exhausted than he had ever felt since six months before, when, finding it more and more difficult to get his breath, he had been secretly admitted to a Dublin hospital to be treated for what was then believed to be a viral infection.

Even the fact that he had recorded a 'This Is Your Life' the previous evening could not explain how weak he felt that Saturday. Grainne, who was spending the weekend in London with him, became so concerned that she made arrangements for him to be admitted to the Cromwell hospital the following Monday for tests.

Eamonn, who had insisted on waiting until the last series of 'This Is Your Life' had ended before agreeing to go into the Dublin hospital, protested that he had another programme to record on the Tuesday.

This time Grainne would not listen. For months now Eamonn had been rapidly and mysteriously losing weight. His family and colleagues were becoming concerned about his deteriorating physical condition. Viewers were starting to telephone Thames Television to inquire about his health. There had been comment in newspapers.

So, for the first time in his career, Eamonn was persuaded to allow one of his shows to be postponed.

By the time he was helped into the car taking him to hospital, he was so weak Grainne had to carry the battered old black Gladstone bag, into which he stuffed scripts, business papers and a change of clothing, which had accompanied him the world over for more than thirty years.

Despite the feeling of weariness, he still managed to remain optimistic that his stay in hospital would not be a long one and, in his room there, he and Grainne talked of the brief anniversary break they planned to spend in the Canary Isles that weekend.

When Grainne called to see him on the Wednesday night they opened a bottle of champagne and drank it as they watched the transmission of the 'This Is Your Life' he had recorded that previous Friday on Irish comedian Jimmy Cricket. Then, as Eamonn started to fall asleep, Grainne kissed him goodnight and quietly let herself out of the room.

Eamonn never woke again. He died in his sleep at 2.15 the following morning. The cause was progressive deterioration of the main heart muscle and the news was broken to his stunned public on the breakfast time news bulletins a few hours later.

One story that reflects the view many of those fans had of Eamonn during his lifetime was inspired by a colleague who had worked with him on 'This Is Your Life' for a number of years.

A journalist who was writing a magazine feature on Eamonn asked the colleague if he had an amusing anecdote about him to help the article along.

'Oh no,' replied the colleague. 'I don't think Eamonn would get involved in anything as risky as an anecdote!'

That was not totally true, of course, because in fact he spent much of his life stumbling in and out of anecdotes.

But on the evidence of what they would be seeing on their screens when they awoke, those imagined Rip Van Winkle viewers would certainly have been prepared to accept that reply – and even more readily had they fallen asleep at the very start of Eamonn's television career rather than just after he had joined ITV.

For they would have realised that when he died, after a television career that had lasted thirty-six years, Eamonn was still presenting the same two shows with which he had started. The only difference was that he was now being seen in colour.

It was Eamonn's greatest frustration, the greatest sadness of his career, that they had to be resurrected in order that his success could continue.

He had asked the BBC to find alternative shows for him as long ago as 1962 when they offered him what was to be his last contract there. They promised they would. But instead, two years later they killed off the 'Life' and the 'Line', offered him nothing in their place and waved him goodbye.

During his career in commercial television he did, of course, try a number of new programmes besides the ill-chosen chat show and the regional magazine but was able to handle none as competently as the two he first started with. The reason, of course, was the script protection those programmes gave him which was absent from the others.

Ironically, both were watched by many more viewers after they had been revived than ever they were when they first reigned. But then Eamonn's life had many an ironic twist, and more ironies were to come with his death.

It was ironic that he should have been succeeded on 'This Is Your Life' by Michael Aspel, because Aspel made no pretence of having enjoyed the experience when Eamonn presented a 'Life' programme on him.

In fact, he disliked it so much he made it clear to members of the production team that, after that, he would rather not be asked even to appear as a guest on anybody else's 'This Is Your Life'. And his dislike was not confined to the fact that a complete stranger – an actor who was at the studios for another purpose but who decided to tag himself onto the end of a 'cavalcade' of Aspel's colleagues – walked on at the very end and shook him heartily by the hand.

It was ironic, too, that Angela Rippon should have taken Eamonn's place as question master on 'What's My Line?'. When she sat in for an indisposed Barbara Kelly for one show not long before Eamonn died the production team felt she had done a lot to liven it up. What they liked was the way she took issue with Eamonn over some of his adjudications, as Gilbert Harding frequently did in the programme's BBC days, and they wanted to offer her a per-manent place on the panel.

Maybe Eamonn did not enjoy her challenges quite so much. In any event, he took the opposite view. 'The woman's a cold fish,' he said, and that was the end of that.

The greatest irony of his life, however, was that it came to an end exactly a quarter-of-a-century after he had introduced Britain's first ever satellite broadcast and in the year that satellite television finally became feasible.

But perhaps not the saddest irony, though. For tragic though his comparatively early death was, maybe after all it was not badly timed. It is doubtful that he would have relished that dizzying satellite assault. Had he lived through its pyrotechnic early years his long career would more than likely have spluttered out completely in the glare of it all and he would then have been soon forgotten.

As it is, despite his shortcomings, it cannot now be taken away from him that Willie Andrews's boy from back-street Dublin over-came inestimable obstacles to become an original, a one-off, a television trail-blazer and – with acknowledgement to devotees of a certain early nineteenth-century art movement – one of television's truly great Pre-Satellites.

For *that* was his life. And that's how he will long be remembered.

Index